## Section Four — Shapes and Area

Symmetry ........................................................................
Properties of 2D Shapes...............................................
Congruence and Similarity .........................................
3D Shapes and Projections ...............................55
Perimeters..........................................................56
Areas .................................................................57
Circles ...............................................................61
Volume...............................................................63
Nets and Surface Area .......................................66

## Section Five — Angles and Geometry

Angles ................................................................67
Five Angle Rules ................................................68
Parallel and Perpendicular Lines .......................70
Polygons and Angles...........................................71
Transformations — Translation ..........................72
Transformations — Reflection ............................73
Transformations — Rotation ..............................74
Transformations — Enlargement ........................75
Similar Shape Problems ......................................76
Loci and Constructions ......................................77
Pythagoras' Theorem .........................................80

## Section Six — Measures

Metric and Imperial Units...................................81
Converting Units ................................................82
Rounding and Estimating Measurements............83
Reading Scales and Timetables ..........................84
Compass Directions and Bearings.......................85
Maps and Scale Drawings ...................................87
Speed .................................................................89
Density................................................................90

## Section Seven — Statistics and Probability

Collecting Data .................................................91
Mean, Median, Mode and Range........................93
Tables, Charts and Pictograms ..........................95
Line Graphs........................................................96
Bar Charts..........................................................97
Pie Charts...........................................................98
Scatter Graphs ................................................100
Stem and Leaf Diagrams ..................................101
Frequency Tables and Averages........................102
Grouped Frequency Tables ...............................103
Times Series.....................................................105
Probability........................................................106

Throughout the book, the more challenging questions are marked like this: **Q1**

Published by CGP

Illustrated by Ruso Bradley, Lex Ward and Ashley Tyson

From original material by Richard Parsons

Contributors:
Gill Allen,
Margaret Carr,
Barbara Coleman,
JE Dodds,
Mark Haslam,
John Lyons,
Gordon Rutter,
Janet West,
Dave Williams,
Philip Wood.

Updated by: Katherine Craig, Ceara Hayden, Sharon Keeley-Holden, Andy Park, Rachel Ward
With thanks to Julie Wakeling for the proofreading.

ISBN: 978 1 84146 563 0

Groovy website: www.cgpbooks.co.uk
Printed by Elanders Ltd, Newcastle upon Tyne.
Jolly bits of clipart from CorelDRAW®

# It's another great book from CGP...

We'll be honest — studying GCSE Maths isn't easy. A lot of the time you'll need to keep working away at questions until you've cracked it.

That's where this book comes in. It's overflowing with practice questions to help you master all the skills you'll need for every topic. It even includes a **free** Online Edition you can read on your computer or tablet.

# CGP — still the best! ☺

Our sole aim here at CGP is to produce the highest quality books — carefully written, immaculately presented and dangerously close to being funny.

Then we work our socks off to get them out to you
— at the cheapest possible prices.

# Contents

## Section One — Numbers

Ordering Numbers and Place Value...............................................1
Addition and Subtraction............................................................2
Multiplying by 10, 100, etc.........................................................3
Dividing by 10, 100, etc.............................................................4
Multiplying Without a Calculator.................................................5
Dividing Without a Calculator.....................................................6
Negative Numbers......................................................................7
Special Number Sequences.........................................................8
Prime Numbers...........................................................................9
Multiples, Factors and Prime Factors........................................10
LCM and HCF............................................................................12
Fractions, Decimals and Percentages........................................13
Fractions...................................................................................14
Fractions and Recurring Decimals............................................18
Proportion Problems..................................................................19
Percentages...............................................................................20
Ratios.......................................................................................23
Rounding Off.............................................................................25
Estimating Calculations.............................................................28
Square Roots and Cube Roots...................................................29
Powers......................................................................................30

## Section Two — Algebra

Algebra......................................................................................31
Solving Equations......................................................................33
Using Formulas..........................................................................34
Making Formulas From Words...................................................35
Rearranging Formulas................................................................36
Number Patterns and Sequences...............................................37
Trial and Improvement..............................................................39
Inequalities................................................................................40
Simultaneous Equations with Graphs........................................41

## Section Three — Graphs

X and Y Coordinates..................................................................42
Midpoint of a Line Segment......................................................43
Straight-Line Graphs..................................................................44
Travel Graphs............................................................................47
Conversion Graphs and Real-Life Graphs..................................48
Quadratic Graphs......................................................................49

## Ordering Numbers and Place Value

**Q1** Put these numbers in ascending (smallest to biggest) order.

a) 23   117   5   374   13   89   67   54   716   18

5   13   18   23   54   67   89   117   374   716

b) 1272   231   817   376   233   46   2319   494   73   1101

46   73   231   233   376   494   817   1101   1272   2319

**Q2** Lewis is writing a cheque for £278.04.
Write this amount in words as it should be written on the cheque.

Two Hundred and Seventy Eight Pounds and four Pence

**Q3** Write down the value of the number 4 in each of these.

For example:   408   *hundreds*

a) 347   tens

b) 41   tens

c) 5478   hundreds

d) 6754   units

e) 4897   thousands

f) 64 098   thousands

g) 745 320   tens of thousands

h) 2 402 876   hundred thousand

i) 6 503 428   hundreds

j) 1.64   hundredths

k) 53.42   tenths

l) 2.524   thousandths

**Q4** Put these values in order of size — from the smallest to the largest.

a) 3.42   4.23   2.43   3.24   2.34   4.32

2.34   2.43   3.24   3.42   4.23   4.32

b) 6.7   6.704   6.64   6.642   6.741

6.64   6.642   6.7   6.704   6.741

> Always look at the whole number part first, then the first digit after the decimal point, then the next etc.

c) 1002.8   102.8   1008.2   1020.8   108.2

102.8   108.2   1002.8   1008.2   1020.8

d) £400.20   £402.22   £402.02   £400.02   £402.20

400.02   400.20   402.02   402.20   402.22

# Addition and Subtraction

NO CALCULATORS HERE! ALWAYS put the numbers in COLUMNS when you're adding or subtracting... and check the UNITS, TENS & HUNDREDS line up.

**Q1** Do these questions as quickly as you can:

a)   26
    +15
     41

b)   34
    +72
    106

c)   63
    +32
     95

d)   75
    +48
    123

e)   238
    + 56
    294

f)   528
    +196
    724

g)   36
    −13
     23

h)   45
    −23
     22

i)   89
    −24
     65

j)   ⁷80
    −42
     68

k)   687
    −235
    452

l)   ³843
    −516
    327

**Q2** Fill in the missing digits:

a)   6 5
    −3 [1]
    [3] 4

b)   7 3 [9]
    −2 [1] 4
    [5] 2 5

c)   ⁶8 ⁷[1]
    −6 3 2
    2 [8] 9

d)   ³¹⁴[ ]5 6
    −2 7 8
    1 [7] [8]

**Q3** Sally bought a new car for £11 995.
Road tax for the car cost her £125, and insurance cost £327.
Work out the total cost of buying, taxing and insuring the car.

11,995
   327
   125
£12,447

**Q4** Hayley has £4127 in her savings account.
She withdraws £530 for a holiday and £328 to pay for home insurance.
How much does she have left in her savings?

⁸3597
 328
3269

£3269

³¹⁰
4127
 530
3597

**Q5** Work out the answers without using a calculator.

a)   2.4
    +3.2
    5.6

b)   3.5
    +4.6
    8.1

c)   6.2
    + 5.9
    12.1

d)   7.34
    + 6.07
    13.41

e)   9.08
    +4.93
    14.01

f)   15.73
    +25.08
    40.81

g)   ⁵6.2
    − 1.5
    4.7

h)   ⁷8.6
    − 3.9
    4.7

i)   ⁶7.0
    − 1.6
    5.4

j)   ²13.6
    − 12.7
    00.9

k)   ⁰³14.65
    − 4.70
    9.95

l)   ⁷¹²8.34
    − 4.65
    3.69

**Q6** Peter bought 2 cups of tea, a cup of coffee, a cheese burger and a bacon butty.
Work out the total cost without using a calculator.

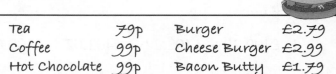

| Tea | 79p | Burger | £2.79 |
| Coffee | 99p | Cheese Burger | £2.99 |
| Hot Chocolate | 99p | Bacon Butty | £1.79 |

£7.35

# Multiplying by 10, 100, etc.

Multiplying by 10, 100 or 1000 moves each digit 1, 2 or 3 places to the left —
you just fill the rest of the space with zeros.  Do not use a calculator for this page.

Fill in the missing numbers.

**Q1**  **a)** 6 × [10] = 60            **b)** 0.07 × [10] = 0.7

**c)** 6 × [100] = 600            **d)** 0.07 × [100] = 7

**e)** 6 × [1000] = 6000            **f)** 0.07 × [1000] = 70

no calculators!!

**Q2**  Which number is ten times as large as 25?  ...250...

**Q3**  Which number is one hundred times as large as 93?  ...9300...

**Q4**  **a)** 8 × 10 = ...80...            **b)** 34 × 100 = 3400            **c)** 52 × 100 = 5200

**d)** 9 × 1000 = 9000            **e)** 436 × 1000 = 436000            **f)** 0.2 × 10 = 2

**g)** 6.9 × 10 = 69            **h)** 4.73 × 100 = 473

**Q5**  For a school concert chairs are put out in rows of 10.
How many will be needed for 16 rows?  ...160...

**Q6**   £2.99 EACH

How much do 10 chickens cost?  £29.90

**Q7**  A school buys calculators for £2.45 each.
How much will 100 cost?  £245.00

**Q8**  **a)** 20 × 30 = ...600...            **b)** 40 × 700 = 48000            **c)** 250 × 20 = 5000

**d)** 6000 × 210 = 1,260,000            **e)** 18 000 × 500 = 9,000,000

**Q9**   A shop bought 700 bars of chocolate for £0.43 each.
How much did they cost altogether?

£301

# Dividing by 10, 100, etc.

Dividing by 10, 100 or 1000 moves each digit 1, 2 or 3 places to the right.

Answer these questions <u>without</u> using a calculator:

**Q1**  **a)** 30 ÷ 10 = ....3....  **b)** 43 ÷ 10 = ..H.3..  **c)** 5.8 ÷ 10 = 0.58

**d)** 63.2 ÷ 10 = ..6.32..  **e)** 0.5 ÷ 10 = ..0.05..  **f)** 400 ÷ 100 = ..H..

**g)** 423 ÷ 100 = ..H.23..  **h)** 228.6 ÷ 100 = 2.286  **i)** 61.5 ÷ 100 = ..0.615..

**j)** 2.96 ÷ 100 = 0.0296  **k)** 6000 ÷ 1000 = ..6..  **l)** 6334 ÷ 1000 = 6.33H

**m)** 753.6 ÷ 1000 = ..0...  **n)** 8.15 ÷ 1000 = ........  **o)** 80 ÷ 20 = ........

**p)** 860 ÷ 20 = ........  **q)** 2400 ÷ 300 = ........  **r)** 480 ÷ 40 = ........

**s)** 860 ÷ 200 = ........  **t)** 63.9 ÷ 30 = ........

**Q2**  Ten people share a Lottery win of £62. How much should each person receive?

**Q3**  Blackpool Tower is 158 m tall. A model of it is being built to a scale of 1 : 100. How tall should the model be?

Millom

**Q4**  A box of 40 chocolates contains 56 g of saturated fat. How much saturated fat is there in 1 chocolate?

**Q5**  Mark went on holiday to France. He exchanged £300 for 342 euros to spend while he was there. How many euros did he get for each £1?

# Negative Numbers

**Q1** Write these numbers in the correct position on the number line below:

−4   3   2   −3   −5   1

●   ●   ●   ●   ●   ●   ●   ●   ●   ●

**0**

**Q2** Put the correct symbol, < or >, between the following pairs of numbers:

**a)** 4   −8

**b)** −6   −2

**c)** −8   −7

< means 'less than',
> means 'more than'.

**d)** −3   −6

**e)** −1   1

**f)** −3.6   −3.7

**Q3** Rearrange the following numbers in order of size, largest first:

−2   2   0.5   −1.5   −8   .......   .......   .......   .......   .......

**Q4 a)** The weather forecast says that the current temperature is −3 °C, but could reach −5 °C in the next few hours. Does this mean that it is going to get colder or warmer?

.................................

**b)** The next day, the forecast says that the temperature is currently −4 °C and will fall by 5 °C overnight. What is the forecast overnight temperature?

.................................

Answer these questions <u>without</u> using your calculator.

**Q5** Work out:

**a)** −6 × 1 = ............

**b)** −8 + 12 = ............

**c)** −8 ÷ 8 = ............

**d)** −70 − 3 = ............

**e)** −100 ÷ 10 = ............

**f)** 5 × −2 = ............

**Q6** Work out:

**a)** −3 + −4 + 1 = ............

**b)** 8 − 9 + −1 = ............

**c)** −10 − −12 + −1 = ............

**d)** 3 + −6 − −5 = ............

It can help to draw a number line to count along, so you can see what you're doing.

# Special Number Sequences

There are five special sequences you need to know:
EVENS, ODDS, SQUARES, CUBES and POWERS.

EVEN   SQUARE   ODD   CUBE

**Q1**    What are these sequences called, and what are their next 3 terms?

**a)** 2, 4, 6, 8, ...

.........................................................................................................

**b)** 1, 3, 5, 7, ...

.........................................................................................................

**c)** 1, 4, 9, 16, ...

.........................................................................................................

**d)** 1, 8, 27, 64, ...

.........................................................................................................

**Q2**    The following sequences are described in words.  Write down their first four terms.

**a)** The powers of 2 starting from 32.

.........................................................................................................

**b)** The cube numbers starting from 1.

.........................................................................................................

**c)** The squares of odd numbers starting from $7^2 = 49$.

.........................................................................................................

**d)** The powers of 10 starting from 1000.

.........................................................................................................

# Prime Numbers

Basically, prime numbers don't divide by anything (except 1 and themselves).
5 is prime — it will only divide by 1 or 5. 1 is an exception to this rule — it is not prime.

**Q1** Write down the first ten prime numbers. ....................................................................

**Q2** Give a reason for 27 not being a prime number. ................................................................

**Q3** Using any or all of the figures **1, 2, 3, 7** write down:

    **a)** the smallest prime number ................

    **b)** a prime number greater than 20 ................

    **c)** a prime number between 10 and 20 ................

    **d)** two prime numbers whose sum is 20 .......... , ..........

    **e)** a number that is not prime ................

**Q4** Find all the prime numbers between 40 and 50. ..............................................................

**Q5** In the <u>ten by ten square</u> opposite, ring all the prime numbers.

The first three have been done for you.

| 1 | ②| ③| 4 | ⑤| 6 | 7 | 8 | 9 | 10 |
|---|---|---|---|---|---|---|---|---|---|
| 11 | 12 | 13 | 14 | 15 | 16 | 17 | 18 | 19 | 20 |
| 21 | 22 | 23 | 24 | 25 | 26 | 27 | 28 | 29 | 30 |
| 31 | 32 | 33 | 34 | 35 | 36 | 37 | 38 | 39 | 40 |
| 41 | 42 | 43 | 44 | 45 | 46 | 47 | 48 | 49 | 50 |
| 51 | 52 | 53 | 54 | 55 | 56 | 57 | 58 | 59 | 60 |
| 61 | 62 | 63 | 64 | 65 | 66 | 67 | 68 | 69 | 70 |
| 71 | 72 | 73 | 74 | 75 | 76 | 77 | 78 | 79 | 80 |
| 81 | 82 | 83 | 84 | 85 | 86 | 87 | 88 | 89 | 90 |
| 91 | 92 | 93 | 94 | 95 | 96 | 97 | 98 | 99 | 100 |

**Q6** A school ran three evening classes: <u>judo, karate and kendo.</u>
The judo class had 29 pupils, the karate class had 27 and the kendo class 23.
For which classes would the teacher have difficulty dividing the pupils into equal groups?

.................................................................

**Q7** Find three sets of three prime numbers which add up to the following numbers:

**10** ........./ ........./ ........    **29** ........./ ........./ ........    **41** ........./ ........./ ........

# Multiples, Factors and Prime Factors

The multiples of a number are its times table — if you need multiples of
more than one number, do them separately then pick the ones in both lists.

**Q1** What are the first five multiples of:

**a)** 4? ...............................................................

**b)** 7? ...............................................................

**c)** 12? .............................................................

**d)** 18? .............................................................

**Q2** Find a number which is a multiple of:

> *A quick way to do these is just to multiply the numbers together.*

**a)** 2 and 6 .........................................................

**b)** 7 and 5 .........................................................

**c)** 2 and 3 and 7 .................................................

**d)** 4 and 5 and 9 .................................................

**Q3** Steven is making cheese straws for a dinner party. There will be **either** six or eight
people at the party. He wants to be able to share the cheese straws out equally.
How many cheese straws should he make?

> *There's more than one right answer to this question.*

...............................................

**Q4** **a)** Find a number which is a multiple of 3 and 8 ...........................................................

**b)** Find another number which is a multiple of 3 and 8 ...........................................................

**c)** Find another number which is a multiple of 3 and 8 ...........................................................

**Q5** Which of these numbers 14, 20, 22, 35, 50, 55, 70, 77, 99 are multiples of:

**a)** 2? ...........................       **b)** 5? ...........................

**c)** 7? ...........................       **d)** 11? ...........................

# Multiples, Factors and Prime Factors

**Q6**   Circle all the factors of 360 in this list of numbers.

     1    2    3    4    5    6    7    8    9    10

**Q7**   48 students went on a geography field trip. Their teachers split them into equal groups. Suggest five different ways that the teachers might have split up the students:

.................. groups of ..................       .................. groups of ..................

.................. groups of ..................       .................. groups of ..................

.................. groups of ..................

**Q8**   Daniel is tiling his bathroom using small square tiles. He wants to put a solid rectangle of blue tiles over his bath. Daniel has 42 blue tiles in total.

  **a)** How could he arrange all 42 tiles to make the longest rectangle? ......................................

  **b)** How could he arrange all 42 tiles to make the squarest rectangle? ......................................

**Q9**   **a)** What is the biggest number that is a factor of both 42 and 18?

    ........................................................................................................

  **b)** What is the smallest number that has both 4 and 18 as factors?

    ........................................................................................................

**Q10**   Complete the factor trees below to express each number as a product of prime factors. The first one has been done for you.

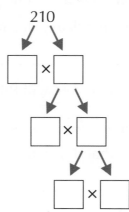

$60 = 2 \times 2 \times 3 \times 5$

$88 = 2 \times 2 \times \ldots \times \ldots$      $210 = \ldots \times \ldots \times \ldots \times \ldots$

# LCM and HCF

**Top tip**

The Lowest Common Multiple (LCM) is the **SMALLEST** number that will **DIVIDE BY ALL** the numbers in question.

The Highest Common Factor (HCF) is the **BIGGEST** number that will **DIVIDE INTO ALL** the numbers in question.

**Q1**   **a)**  List the <u>first ten</u> multiples of 6, <u>starting at 6</u>.

...............................................................................................................

   **b)**  List the <u>first ten</u> multiples of 5, <u>starting at 5</u>.

...............................................................................................................

   **c)**  What is the <u>LCM</u> of 5 and 6?  ...............................

**Q2**   For each set of numbers find the HCF.

   **a)** 3, 5                        **c)** 10, 15                        **e)** 14, 21
   .............................            .............................            .............................

   **b)** 6, 8                        **d)** 27, 48                        **f)** 11, 33, 121
   .............................            .............................            .............................

**Q3**   For each set of numbers, find the LCM.

   **a)** 3, 5                        **c)** 10, 15                        **e)** 14, 21
   .............................            .............................            .............................

   **b)** 6, 8                        **d)** 15, 18                        **f)** 11, 33, 44
   .............................            .............................            .............................

**Q4**   Lars, Rita and Alan regularly go swimming.  Lars goes every 2 days, Rita goes every 3 days and Alan goes every 5 days.  They <u>all</u> went swimming together on Friday 1st June.

*This is an LCM question in disguise.*

   **a)**  On what date will Lars and Rita next go swimming together?

...............................................................................................................

   **b)**  On what date will Rita and Alan next go swimming together?

...............................................................................................................

   **c)**  On what day of the week will all 3 next go swimming together?

...............................................................................................................

   **d)**  Which of the 3 (if any) will go swimming on 15th June?

...............................................................................................................

*SECTION ONE — NUMBERS*

# Fractions, Decimals and Percentages

**Q1**      Change these fractions to decimals:

     **a)** $\frac{1}{2}$ ........
         **b)** $\frac{3}{4}$ ........
         **c)** $\frac{7}{10}$ ........
         **d)** $\frac{19}{20}$ ........

     **e)** $\frac{1}{100}$ ........
         **f)** $\frac{3}{8}$ ........
         **g)** $\frac{2}{1000}$ ........
         **h)** $\frac{1}{3}$ ........

**Q2**      Change these fractions to percentages:

     **a)** $\frac{1}{4}$ ........
         **b)** $\frac{3}{10}$ ........
         **c)** $\frac{4}{5}$ ........
         **d)** $\frac{12}{25}$ ........

     **e)** $\frac{8}{100}$ ........
         **f)** $\frac{2}{40}$ ........
         **g)** $\frac{7}{8}$ ........
         **h)** $\frac{11}{30}$ ........

**Q3**      Change these decimals to percentages:

     **a)** 0.62 ............
         **b)** 0.74 ............
         **c)** 0.4 ............
         **d)** 0.9 ............

     **e)** 0.07 ............
         **f)** 0.02 ............
         **g)** 0.125 ............
         **h)** 0.987 ............

**Q4**      Change these percentages to decimals:

     **a)** 25% ............
         **b)** 49% ............
         **c)** 3% ............
         **d)** 30% ............

**Q5**      Change these percentages to fractions (in their lowest terms):

     **a)** 75% ............
         **b)** 60% ............
         **c)** 15% ............
         **d)** 53% ............

**Q6**      Change these decimals to fractions (in their lowest terms):

     **a)** 0.5 ............
         **b)** 0.8 ............
         **c)** 0.19 ............
         **d)** 0.25 ............

     **e)** 0.64 ............
         **f)** 0.06 ............
         **g)** 0.125 ............
         **h)** 0.075 ............

**A FRACTION IS A DECIMAL IS A PERCENTAGE —**
they're all just different ways of saying "a bit of" something.

# Fractions

To make an **EQUIVALENT** fraction, you've got to multiply the **TOP** (numerator) and **BOTTOM** (denominator) by the **SAME THING**.

**Q1** Shade in the correct number of sections to make these diagrams equivalent.

$\dfrac{1}{4} =$

$\dfrac{1}{3} =$

**Q2** Write in the missing numbers to reduce these fractions to their simplest forms.

For example 7/14 = 1/2

**a)** 4/16 = 1/ 4

**b)** 9/12 = 3/ 3

**c)** 2/6 = 1 /3

**d)** 8/12 = 2/ 4

**e)** 6/18 = 1/ 6

**f)** 24/32 = 3/.......

**Q3** Write in the missing numbers to make each list equivalent.

**a)** 1/2 = 2/...... = ...... /6 = ...... /8 = 5/10 = 25/...... = ...... /70 = ...... /100

**b)** 200/300 = 100/ ...... = ...... /15 = 40/ ...... = 120/180 = ...... /9 = ...... /3

**c)** 7/10 = 14/ ...... = ...... /30 = 210/ ...... = 49/ ...... = ...... /20

**d)** 19/20 = ...... /80 = 38/ ...... = 57/ ...... = ...... /100 = ...... /1000

**Q4** Write these sets of fractions in order of size, starting with the smallest:

**a)** 1/5, 3/10 ........................................

**b)** 3/7, 6/21 ........................................

**c)** 11/15, 4/6, 4/5 ........................................

**d)** 1/3, 5/12, 4/6 ........................................

**Q5** Healthybix cereal contains 6 g of sugar in every 40 g. Special F cereal contains 8 g of sugar in every 50 g. Joanna is on a diet and wants to buy the breakfast cereal with the lowest fraction of sugar. Which cereal should she buy?

........................................

# Fractions

**Q6**   Write down the following quantities:

**a)** Half of 12 = ........          **b)** Quarter of 24 = ........          **c)** Third of 30 = ........

**d)** 1/4 of 44 = ........          **e)** 3/4 of 60 = ........          **f)** 2/3 of 6 = ........

**Q7**   Calculate the following fractions without using a calculator:

e.g. 1/3 of 18 = 18 ÷ 3 = $\underline{6}$

**a)** 1/8 of 32 = ........ ÷ 8 = ........          **b)** 1/10 of 50 = ........ ÷ 10 = ........

**c)** 1/12 of 144 = ........ ÷ ........ = ........          **d)** 1/25 of 75 = ........ ÷ ........ = ........

**e)** 1/30 of 180 = ........ ÷ ........ = ........          **f)** 1/27 of 540 = ........ ÷ ........ = ........

**Q8**   Calculate the following fractions without using a calculator:
e.g. 2/5 of 50        50 ÷ 5 = 10        2 × 10 = $\underline{20}$

**a)** 2/3 of 60          60 ÷ 3 = ........          2 × ........ = ........

**b)** 4/5 of 25          25 ÷ ........ = ........          4 × ........ = ........

**c)** 7/9 of 63          ........ ÷ ........ = ........          ........ × ........ = ........

**d)** 3/10 of 100          ........ ÷ ........ = ........          ........ × ........ = ........

**e)** 12/19 of 760          ........ ÷ ........ = ........          ........ × ........ = ........

**f)** 6/9 of £1.80          ........ ÷ ........ = ........          ........ × ........ = £........ or ........ p

**g)** 10/18 of £9.00          ........ ÷ ........ = ........          ........ × ........ = £........

**Q9**   A return car journey from Lancaster to Stoke uses 5/6 of a tank of petrol.
How much does this cost, if it costs £54 for a full tank of petrol?

........................

**Q10**   Peter works in a clothes shop.  He gets a staff discount and only has to pay 2/3 of
the price of any item.  How much will a £24 top cost him?

........................

**Q11**   A recipe for 5 people needs 1 kg of potatoes.  Helen reduces the recipe to make
enough for 2 people.  How many kilograms of potatoes does she need?

........................

*SECTION ONE — NUMBERS*

# Fractions

Fraction arithmetic becomes a nice cruise in the park, once you've learned the rules for dealing with each type of calculation.

> **MULTIPLYING:** just multiply the <u>tops</u> and the <u>bottoms</u>.
> **DIVIDING:** turn the second fraction <u>upside down</u>, then <u>multiply them</u>.
> **ADDING OR SUBTRACTING:**
> 1) Make the bottom number <u>the same</u> (get "a common denominator")
> 2) Add or subtract the top numbers <u>only</u>.

Answer the following questions <u>without</u> using a calculator.

**Q12** Change these improper fractions to mixed numbers:

a) $\frac{3}{2} =$ ..........     b) $\frac{7}{4} =$ ..........     c) $\frac{8}{3} =$ ..........

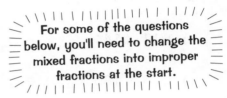
For some of the questions below, you'll need to change the mixed fractions into improper fractions at the start.

Change these mixed numbers to improper fractions:

d) $2\frac{1}{2} =$ ..........     e) $3\frac{1}{3} =$ ..........     f) $1\frac{3}{5} =$ ..........

**Q13** Do the following multiplications, expressing the answers as fractions in their lowest terms:

a) $\frac{4}{3} \times \frac{3}{4}$ .............................     d) $2\frac{1}{2} \times \frac{3}{5}$ .............................

b) $\frac{2}{5} \times \frac{3}{4}$ .............................     e) $10\frac{2}{7} \times \frac{7}{9}$ .............................

c) $\frac{11}{9} \times \frac{6}{5}$ .............................     f) $2\frac{1}{6} \times 3\frac{1}{3}$ .............................

**Q14** Carry out the following divisions, and express each answer in its lowest term:

a) $\frac{1}{4} \div \frac{3}{8}$ .............................     d) $1\frac{1}{2} \div \frac{5}{12}$ .............................

b) $\frac{1}{9} \div \frac{2}{3}$ .............................     e) $10\frac{4}{5} \div \frac{9}{10}$ .............................

c) $\frac{15}{24} \div \frac{6}{5}$ .............................     f) $3\frac{7}{11} \div 1\frac{4}{11}$ .............................

**Q15** Add the two fractions, giving your answer as a fraction in its lowest term:

a) $\frac{7}{8} + \frac{3}{8}$ .....................    b) $\frac{1}{12} + \frac{3}{4}$ .....................    c) $\frac{1}{3} + \frac{3}{4}$ .....................

d) $1\frac{2}{5} + 2\frac{2}{3}$ .....................    e) $\frac{1}{6} + 4\frac{1}{3}$ .....................    f) $1\frac{3}{10} + \frac{2}{5}$ .....................

# Fractions

**Q16** Evaluate the following, giving your answers as mixed numbers:

**a)** $\dfrac{11}{4} - \dfrac{2}{3}$ .......................

**b)** $10 - \dfrac{2}{5}$ .......................

**c)** $1\dfrac{3}{4} - \dfrac{1}{5}$ .......................

**d)** $4\dfrac{2}{3} - \dfrac{7}{9}$ .......................

**e)** $3\dfrac{1}{2} - \dfrac{2}{3}$ .......................

**f)** $8 - \dfrac{1}{8}$ .......................

Try these questions without a calculator:

**Q17** What fraction of 1 hour is:

**a)** 5 minutes? ..............

**b)** 15 minutes? ..............

**c)** 40 minutes? ..............

**Q18** A café employs eighteen girls and twelve boys to wait at tables. Another six boys and nine girls work in the kitchen.

    **a)** What fraction of the <u>kitchen staff</u> are girls? .......................

    **b)** What fraction of the <u>employees</u> are boys? .......................

**Q19** If a TV programme lasts 40 minutes, what fraction of the programme is left after:

**a)** 10 minutes? ..............

**b)** 15 minutes? ..............

**c)** 35 minutes? ..............

# Fractions and Recurring Decimals

Use a calculator for the questions below.

**Q1** If I pay my gas bill within seven days, I get a <u>reduction</u> of an eighth of the price. If my bill is £120, how much can I save? .................

**Q2** Owen gives money to a charity directly from his wages, before tax. One sixth of his monthly earnings goes to the charity, then one fifth of what's left gets deducted as tax. How much money goes to charity and on tax, and how much is left, if he earns £2400?

Charity ........................., Tax ........................., Left over .........................

\ \ \ \ \ \ | | | | | / / / / / /
**Don't get put off by all the padding in the questions — you've just got to pick out the important stuff.**

This is about as scary as fractions get, but don't panic!

| All fractions can be written as <u>**TERMINATING**</u> or <u>**RECURRING** decimals</u> |
|---|

If a fraction's denominator (bottom number) has **PRIME FACTORS** of only 2 and/or 5, then it's a **TERMINATING DECIMAL** — they don't go on forever: e.g. $\frac{1}{10} = \frac{1}{2 \times 5} = 0.1$

If a fraction's denominator has **OTHER PRIME FACTORS**, then it's a **RECURRING DECIMAL** — they have a pattern of numbers that goes on forever: e.g. $\frac{4}{11} = 0.363636... = 0.\dot{3}\dot{6}$

**Q3** <u>Without</u> using a calculator say whether each of these fractions will give a terminating or recurring decimal:

**a)** 1/6 ..............................  **d)** 1/7 ..............................

**b)** 1/10 ..............................  **e)** 1/2 ..............................

**c)** 1/3 ..............................  **f)** 1/5 ..............................

**Q4** Use a <u>calculator</u> to write the following fractions as recurring decimals:

**a)** 4/9 ..............................  **c)** 5/9 ..............................

*Use a calculator to turn the number into a decimal, then look for a repeating pattern...*

**b)** 3/11 ..............................  **d)** 7/11 ..............................

# Proportion Problems

**Remember the golden rule: DIVIDE FOR ONE, THEN TIMES FOR ALL**

**Q1**   7 pencils cost £2.80.  How much will 4 pencils cost?

.......................................................................

**Q2**   Isla is making a chocolate cake using the recipe shown on the right. She wants to make the cake for 10 people.

| Chocolate cake |
| --- |
| (serves 6) |
| 180 g   flour |
| 240 g   sugar |
| 210 g   butter |
| 3          eggs |
| 60 g     cocoa powder |

**a)** How much sugar will she need?

.......................................................................

**b)** How much flour will she need?

.......................................................................

**c)** Isla only has 320 g of butter.  Will this be enough for her cake?

.......................................................................

**Q3**

The small bar of chocolate weighs 50 g and costs 32p.
The large bar weighs 200 g and costs 80p.

**a)** How many grams do you get for 1p from the small bar?

.............................

**b)** How many grams do you get for 1p from the large bar?

.............................

**c)** Which bar gives you more for your money?

.............................

**Q4**   Which of these boxes of eggs is better value for money?

60p                          £1.10                    ...........................................

# Percentages

Finding "something %" of "something-else" is really
quite simple — so you'd better be sure you know how.

| 1) Turn the percentage into a decimal... <br> 2) ... then multiply. | Example: Find 30% of 150. <br> 1)  30% = 30 ÷ 100 = 0.3 <br> 2)  0.3 × 150 = 45 |
|---|---|

**Q1**    Without using a calculator, work out the following percentages:

**a)** 50% of £12 = ...............................    **b)** 25% of £20 = ...............................

**c)** 10% of £50 ...............................    **d)** 5% of £50 = ...............................

**e)** 30% of £50 = ...............................    **f)** 75% of £80 = ...............................

**g)** 10% of 90 cm = ...............................    **h)** 10% of 4.39 kg = ...............................

Now have a go at these using your calculator:

**i)** 8% of £16 = ...............................

**j)** 85% of 740 kg = ...............................

**k)** 40% of 40 minutes = ...............................

A school has 750 pupils.

**l)** If 56% of the pupils are boys, what percentage are girls? ...............................

**m)** How many boys are there in the school? ...............................

**n)** One day, 6% of the pupils were absent.  How many pupils was this? ...............................

**o)** 54% of the pupils have a school lunch, 38% bring sandwiches and the rest go home for lunch.  How many pupils go home for lunch?

...............................

**Q2**    Work out these percentage questions:

**a)** A T-shirt is priced at £18.  Ted has a 15% off voucher to use in the shop.
How much will the T-shirt cost Ted if he uses his voucher?

...............................

**b)** A savings account gains 2.5% interest per year.  How much interest will a saver earn
if they have £200 in their account for a year?

...............................

# Percentages

**Q3**  John bought a new PC.  The tag in the shop said it cost <u>£890 + VAT</u>.
If VAT is charged at 20%, how much did he pay?

.........................................................................................................................................

**Q4**  Admission to Wonder World is <u>£18 for adults</u>.  A child ticket is <u>60%</u> of the adult price.

 **a)** How much will it cost for one adult and 4 children to enter Wonder World?

.........................................................................................................................................

 **b)** How much will two adults and three children spend on entrance tickets?

.........................................................................................................................................

**Q5**  Daphne earns an annual wage of £18 900.  She doesn't pay tax on the first £6400 that
she earns.  How much income tax does she pay if the rate of tax is:

 **a)** 20% ? ........................        **b)** 40% ? ........................

**Q6**  The cost of a train ticket changes with inflation.  If the annual rate of inflation is 2% and
my train ticket home cost £28 last year, how much will my ticket home cost this year?

.........................................................................................................................................

**Q7**  A double-glazing salesman is paid 10% commission on every sale he makes.
In addition he is paid a £50 bonus if the sale is over £500.

 **a)** If a customer buys £499 worth of windows from the
salesman, what is his <u>commission</u>?

.................................................................

 **b)** How much extra will he earn if he persuades the
customer in **a)** to spend an extra £20?

.................................................................

 **c)** How much does he earn if he sells £820 worth of
windows?

.................................................................

**Q8**  Bed & breakfast £37 per person.  Evening meal £15 per person.

THE PICKLED PARROT

2 people stay at The Pickled Parrot for 2 nights and have an evening meal
each night.  How much is the total cost, if VAT is added at 20% ?

.........................................................................................................................................

# Percentages

Divide the new amount by the old, then × 100... or if you've been practising on your calc, you'll know you can just press the % button for the 2nd bit...

**Q9**     Express each of the following as a percentage.  Round off if necessary.

a) £6 of £12 = ....................

b) £4 of £16 = ....................

c) 600 kg of 750 kg = ....................

d) 6 hours of one day = ....................

e) 1 month of a year = ....................

f) 25 m of 65 m = ....................

**Q10**    Calculate the percentage saving of the following:

e.g. Trainers: Was £72  Now £56  Saved ..£16.. of £72 = ....22....%

a) Jeans: Was £45 Now £35  Saved ......... of £45 = ..........%

b) CD: Was £14.99 Now £12.99 Saved .......... of ......... = ..........%

c) Shirt: Was £27.50 Now £22.75 Saved .......... of .......... = ..........%

d) TV: Was £695 Now £435 Saved .................... = ..........%

e) Microwave: Was £132 Now £99 Saved ............... = ..........%

**Q11** a) If Andy Hurray won 3 out of the 5 sets in the Wimbledon Men's Final, what percentage of the sets did he not win?

...................................................................................%

b) Of a resort's 25 000 tourists last Summer, 23 750 were between 16 and 30 years old. What percentage of the tourists were not in this age group?

...................................................................................%

c) Jeff went on a diet.  At the start he weighed 92 kg, after one month he weighed 84 kg. What is his percentage weight loss?

...................................................................................%

d) In their first game of the season, Nowcastle had 24 567 fans watching the game. By the final game there were 32 741 fans watching.  What is the percentage increase in the number of fans?

...................................................................................%

# Ratios

Ratios compare quantities of the same kind — so if the units aren't mentioned, they've got to be the same in each bit of the ratio.

**Q1** Write each of these ratios in its simplest form. The first one is done for you.

   **a)** 4 to 6           **b)** 15 to 21         **c)** 72 to 45        **d)** 24 cm to 36 cm

     2 : 3               ...... : ......          ....... : ......        ...... : ......

             **e)** 350 g to 2 kg         **f)** 42p to £1.36

               ...... : ......             ...... : ......

> Watch out for ones like e) and f) — you need to make the units the same first.

**Q2** To make grey paint, black and white paint are mixed in the ratio 5:3. How much black paint would be needed with:

   **a)** 6 litres of white? ....................................

   **b)** 12 litres of white? ....................................

   **c)** 21 litres of white? ....................................

**Q3** To make salad dressing you mix olive oil and vinegar in the ratio 5:2. How much olive oil is needed with:

   **a)** 10 ml of vinegar? ................................      **b)** 30 ml of vinegar? ................................

   **c)** 42 ml of vinegar? ................................

**Q4** Sarah works as a waitress. Each week, she splits her wage into spending money and savings in the ratio 7:3.

   **a)** One week, Sarah earns £130.
       How much should she put in her savings that week? ...................................

   **b)** The next week, Sarah put £42 into her savings.
       How much did she earn in total that week? ...................................

**Q5** The ratio of men to women at a football match was 11:4. How many men were there if there were:

   **a)** 2000 women? ................................      **b)** 8460 women? ................................

24

# Ratios

**Q6**  Divide each of the following quantities in the given ratio.

For example:

£400 in the ratio 1 : 4      1 + 4 = 5                    £400 ÷ 5 = £80

   <u>1 × £80 = £80 and 4 × £80 = £320</u>    <u>£80 : £320</u>


**a)** 100 g in the ratio 1 : 4      ...... + ....... = .......        ....... ÷ ....... = .......

....... × ....... = ....... and ....... × ....... = .......

= ....... : .......

**b)** 500 m in the ratio 2 : 3 = ...................................................................  ....... : .......

**c)** £12 000 in the ratio 1 : 2 = ...................................................................  ....... : ......

**d)** 6.3 kg in the ratio 3 : 4 = ...................................................................  ....... : .......

**e)** £8.10 in the ratio 4 : 5 = ...................................................................  ....... : .......

**Q7**  Now try these…

**a)** Adam and Mags win £24 000.  They split the money in the
ratio 1 : 5.  How much does Adam get?

..........................................................................

**b)** Sunil, Paul and Rita work in a restaurant.  Any tips they earn are split
in the ratio 3 : 4 : 2.  One night they earned £36 in tips between them.
Who got the most tip money?  How much did they get?

.............................................................. got £.......................

**c)** The total distance covered in a triathlon (swimming, cycling and running) is 15 km.
It is split in the ratio 2 : 3 : 5.  How far is each section?

Swimming = ......................., cycling = ......................., running = .......................

A great way to check your answer works is to add up the individual
quantities — they should add up to the original amount.

*SECTION ONE — NUMBERS*

# Rounding Off

**Q1**    Round the following to the nearest whole number:

**a)** 2.9 ..........          **b)** 26.8 ..........          **c)** 2.24 ..........

**d)** 11.11 ..........        **e)** 6.347 ..........        **f)** 43.5 ..........

**g)** 9.99 ..........         **h)** 0.41 ..........

> Nearest <u>whole number</u> means you look at the digit after the decimal point to decide whether to round up or down.

**Q2**    An average family has 2.3 children, how many children is this to the nearest whole number?

...............

**Q3**    By the time she is 25 the average woman will have driven 4.72 cars.  What is this to the nearest whole number?

...............

**Q4**    Give these amounts to the nearest pound:

**a)** £4.29 ..........         **b)** £16.78 ..........        **c)** £12.06 ..........

**d)** £7.52 ..........         **e)** £0.93 ..........         **f)** £14.50 ..........

**g)** £7.49 ..........         **h)** £0.28 ..........

**Q5**    Give these amounts to the nearest hour:

**a)** 2 hours 12 minutes ...............................          **b)** 36 minutes ...............................

**c)** 12 hours 12 minutes ...............................          **d)** 29 minutes ...............................

**e)** 100 minutes ...............................          **f)** 90 minutes ...............................

# Rounding Off

**Q6** Round off these numbers to the nearest 10:

**a)** 23 ..............     **b)** 78 ..............     **c)** 65 ..............     **d)** 99 ..............

**e)** 118 ..............     **f)** 243 ..............     **g)** 958 ..............     **h)** 1056 ..............

**Q7** Round off these numbers to the nearest 100:

**a)** 627 ..............     **b)** 791 ..............     **c)** 199 ..............     **d)** 450 ..............

**e)** 1288 ..............     **f)** 3329 ..............     **g)** 2993 ..............

**Q8** Crowd sizes at sports events are often given exactly in newspapers. Round off these exact crowd sizes to the nearest 1000:

**a)** 23 324 ..............

**b)** 36 844 ..............

**c)** 49 752 ..............

**Q9** Round off these numbers to 1 decimal place (1 d.p.):

**a)** 7.34 ..............     **b)** 8.47 ..............     **c)** 12.08 ..............     **d)** 28.03 ..............

**e)** 9.35 ..............     **f)** 14.618 ..............     **g)** 30.409 ..............

**Q10** Round off the following to 2 d.p.:

**a)** 17.363 ..............     **b)** 38.057 ..............     **c)** 0.735 ..............

**d)** 5.99823 ..............     **e)** 4.297 ..............     **f)** 7.0409 ..............

# Rounding Off

**Q11**    Now round these to 3 d.p.:

    **a)** 6.3534 ......................

    **b)** 81.64471 ......................

    **c)** 0.0075 ......................

    **d)** 53.26981 ......................

    **e)** 754.39962 ......................

    **f)** 0.000486 ......................

**Q12**    Seven people have a meal in a restaurant.  The total
bill comes to £60.  If they share the bill equally,
how much should each of them pay?
Round your answer to 2 d.p.

    ......................................

The <u>1st significant figure</u>
of any number is the first
digit which isn't zero.

**Q13**    Round these numbers to 1 significant figure.

    **a)** 12 ......................

    **b)** 530 ......................

    **c)** 1379 ......................

    **d)** 0.021 ......................

    **e)** 1829.62 ......................

    **f)** 0.296 ......................

**Q14**    Round these numbers to 3 significant figures.

    **a)** 1379 ......................

    **b)** 1329.62 ......................

    **c)** 0.296 ......................

    **d)** 0.02139 ......................

**Q15**    $K = 56.762$
Write $K$ correct to:

    **a)** three significant figures ......................

    **b)** two significant figures ......................

    **c)** one significant figure. ......................

# Estimating Calculations

Round off to **NICE EASY CONVENIENT NUMBERS**, then use them to do the sum.  Easy peasy.

**Q1**    Estimate the answers to these questions...

For example:   $12 \times 21$   $\underline{10 \times 20 = 200}$

**a)** $18 \times 12$   ........ × ........ = ........

**b)** $23 \times 21$   ........ × ........ = ........

**c)** $57 \times 46$   ........ × ........ = ........

**d)** $98 \times 145$   ........ × ........ = ........

**e)** $11 \div 4$   ........ ÷ ........ = ........

**f)** $22 \div 6$   ........ ÷ ........ = ........

**g)** $97 \div 9$   ........ ÷ ........ = ........

**h)** $147 \div 14$   ........ ÷ ........ = ........

**i)** $195 \times 205$   ........ × ........ = ........

**j)** $545 \times 301$   ........ × ........ = ........

**k)** $901 \div 33$   ........ ÷ ........ = ........

**l)** $1207 \div 598$   ........ ÷ ........ = ........

**Q2**    Andy earns a salary of £24 108 each year.

**a)** Estimate how much Andy earns per month.                £ ....................

**b)** Andy is hoping to get a bonus this year.  The bonus is calculated as £1017 plus 9.7% of each worker's salary.  Estimate the amount of Andy's bonus.

£ ....................

**c)** Andy pays 10.14% of his regular salary into a pension scheme.  Estimate how much money he has left per year after making his pension payments.

£ ....................

**Q3**    Estimate the answers to these calculations:

**a)** $\dfrac{58.3 \times 11.4}{5.1}$ = ........................

**b)** $\dfrac{33.7 \times 6.2}{2.3}$ = ........................

**c)** $\dfrac{18.4 \times 4.8}{3.9}$ = ........................

**d)** $\dfrac{17.6 \times 29.5}{3.7}$ = ........................

**e)** $\dfrac{2.9 \times 48.3}{0.476}$ = ........................

**f)** $\dfrac{5.4 \times 8.32}{0.139}$ = ........................

**g)** $\dfrac{7.2 \times 97.5}{0.521}$ = ........................

**h)** $\dfrac{4.5 \times 19.3}{0.199}$ = ........................

# Square Roots and Cube Roots

Square root just means "WHAT NUMBER TIMES ITSELF (i.e. 2×2) GIVES..."
The square roots of 64 are 8 and −8 because 8×8=64 and -8×-8=64.

Cube root means "WHAT NUMBER TIMES BY ITSELF AND THEN BY ITSELF
AGAIN (i.e. 2×2×2) GIVES ..." The cube root of 27 is 3 because 3×3×3=27.

Square roots always have a + and − answer, cube roots only have 1 answer.

**Q1**   Use the $\sqrt{\phantom{x}}$ button on your calculator to find the following <u>positive</u> square roots to the nearest whole number.

   **a)** $\sqrt{60}$ = ..........

   **b)** $\sqrt{19}$ = ..........

   **c)** $\sqrt{34}$ = ..........

   **d)** $\sqrt{200}$ = ..........

   **e)** $\sqrt{520}$ = ..........

   **f)** $\sqrt{75}$ = ..........

   **g)** $\sqrt{750}$ = ..........

   **h)** $\sqrt{0.9}$ = ..........

   **i)** $\sqrt{170}$ = ..........

   **j)** $\sqrt{7220}$ = ..........

   **k)** $\sqrt{1\,000\,050}$ = ..........

   **l)** $\sqrt{27}$ = ..........

**Q2**   Without using a calculator, write down both answers to each of the following:

   **a)** $\sqrt{4}$ = ..........

   **b)** $\sqrt{16}$ = ..........

   **c)** $\sqrt{9}$ = ..........

   **d)** $\sqrt{49}$ = ..........

   **e)** $\sqrt{25}$ = ..........

   **f)** $\sqrt{100}$ = ..........

   **g)** $\sqrt{144}$ = ..........

   **h)** $\sqrt{64}$ = ..........

   **i)** $\sqrt{81}$ = ..........

**Q3**   Use your calculator to find the following:

   **a)** $\sqrt[3]{4096}$ = ..........

   **b)** $\sqrt[3]{1728}$ = ..........

   **c)** $\sqrt[3]{1331}$ = ..........

   **d)** $\sqrt[3]{1\,000\,000}$ = ..........

   **e)** $\sqrt[3]{1}$ = ..........

   **f)** $\sqrt[3]{0.125}$ = ..........

**Q4**   Without using a calculator, find the value of the following:

   **a)** $\sqrt[3]{64}$ = ....................................

   **b)** $\sqrt[3]{27}$ = ....................................

   **c)** $\sqrt[3]{1000}$ = ....................................

   **d)** $\sqrt[3]{8}$ = ....................................

**Q5**   Nida is buying a small storage box online.  She sees a cube box with volume of 125 cm³.  What is the length of each box edge?

   ................................................................................................

**Q6**   A farmer is buying fencing to surround a square field of area 3600 m².
What length of fencing does he need to buy?

   ................................................................................................

# Powers

**Q1** Complete the following:

    **a)** $2^4 = 2 \times 2 \times 2 \times 2 = $ .........

    **b)** $10^3 = 10 \times 10 \times 10 = $ .........

    **c)** $3^5 = 3 \times$ ............... $= $ .........

    **d)** $4^6 = 4 \times$ .................... $= $ .........

    **e)** $1^9 = 1 \times$ .................... $= $ .........

    **f)** $5^6 = 5 \times$ .................... $= $ .........

**Q2** Simplify the following:

    **a)** $2 \times 2 \times 2 \times 2 \times 2 \times 2 \times 2 \times 2 = $ .........

    **b)** $12 \times 12 \times 12 \times 12 \times 12 = $ .........

    **c)** $m \times m \times m = $ .........

    **d)** $y \times y \times y \times y = $ .........

**Q3** Use your <u>calculator</u> to find the exact value of

    **a)** $4^3$ .........    **b)** $10^4$ .........    **c)** $12^5$ .........    **d)** $13^3$ .........

**Q4** Complete the following (the first one has been done for you):

    **a)** $10^2 \times 10^3 = $   $(10 \times 10) \times (10 \times 10 \times 10)$   $= 10^5$

    **b)** $10^3 \times 10^4 = $ ..................................... $= $

    **c)** $10^4 \times 10^2 = $ ..................................... $= $

    **d)** What is the <u>quick method</u> for writing down the final result in **b)** and **c)**?

    .................................................................................................................

**Q5** Complete the following (the first one has been done for you):

    **a)** $2^4 \div 2^2 = \dfrac{(2 \times 2 \times 2 \times 2)}{(2 \times 2)} = 2^2$

    **c)** $4^5 \div 4^3 = \dfrac{(4 \times 4 \times 4 \times 4 \times 4)}{\text{.....................}} = $ .........

    **b)** $2^5 \div 2^2 = \dfrac{(2 \times 2 \times 2 \times 2 \times 2)}{(2 \times 2)} = $ .........

    **d)** $8^5 \div 8^2 = \dfrac{\text{.....................}}{\text{.....................}} = $ .........

    **e)** What is the quick method for writing down the final result in **b)**, **c)** and **d)**?

    .................................................................................................................

**Q6** Write the following as a <u>single term</u>:

    **a)** $10^6 \div 10^4 = $ ...............................

    **b)** $(8^2 \times 8^5) \div 8^3 = $ ...............................

    **c)** $6^{10} \div (6^2 \times 6^3) = $ ...............................

    **d)** $x^2 \times x^3 = $ ...............................

    **e)** $a^5 \times a^4 = $ ...............................

    **f)** $p^4 \times p^5 \times p^6 = $ ...............................

Powers are just a way of writing numbers in shorthand — they come in especially handy with big numbers. Imagine writing out $2^{138}$ — $2 \times 2 \times ... \times 2 \times ... \times 2 \times$ yawn $\times$ zzz...

# Algebra

Algebra can be pretty scary at first. But don't panic — the secret is just to practise lots and lots of questions. Eventually you'll be able to do it without thinking, just like riding a bike. But a lot more fun, obviously...

| **Simplifying** means collecting **like terms** together: | **Expanding** means removing brackets: |
|---|---|
|  $8x^2 + 2x + 4x^2 - x + 4$ becomes $12x^2 + x + 4$ | Eg $4(x + y) = 4x + 4y$ $x(2 + x) = 2x + x^2$ $-(a + b) = -a - b$ |

**Q1**    By collecting like terms, simplify the following. The first one is done for you.

**a)** $6x + 3x - 5 = 9x - 5$

**e)** $3x + 4y + 12x - 5y =$ ...................

**b)** $2x + 3x - 5x =$ ...................

**f)** $11a + 6b + 24a + 18b =$ ...................

**c)** $9f + 16f + 15 - 30 =$ ...................

**g)** $9f + 16g - 15f - 30g =$ ...................

**d)** $14x + 12x - 1 + 2x =$ ...................

**h)** $14a + 12a^2 - 3 + 2a =$ ...................

**Q2**    Simplify the following. The first one is done for you.

**a)** $3x^2 + 5x - 2 + x^2 - 3x = 4x^2 + 2x - 2$

**e)** $2a + 4a^2 - 6a - 3a^2 + 4 =$ ...................

**b)** $5x^2 + 3 + 3x - 4 =$ ...................

**f)** $15 - 3x - 2x^2 - 8 - 2x - x^2 =$ ...................

**c)** $13 + 2x^2 - 4x + x^2 + 5 =$ ...................

**g)** $x^2 + 2x + x^2 + 3x + x^2 + 4x =$ ...................

**d)** $7y - 4 + 6y^2 + 2y - 1 =$ ...................

**h)** $2y^2 + 10y - 7 + 3y^2 - 12y + 1 =$ ...................

**Q3**    Expand the brackets and then simplify if possible. The first one is done for you.

Careful with the minus signs — they multiply both terms in the bracket.

**a)** $2(x + y) = 2x + 2y$

**e)** $-(y - 2) =$ ...................

**b)** $4(x - 3) =$ ...................

**f)** $x(y + 2) =$ ...................

**c)** $8(x^2 + 2) =$ ...................

**g)** $x(x + y + z) =$ ...................

**d)** $-2(x + 5) =$ ...................

**h)** $8(a + b) + 2(a + 2b) =$ ...................

# Algebra

**FACTORISING** — it's just putting the brackets back in. All you have to do is look for common factors that will go into every term. The factors can be numbers or letters.

Example: Factorise $4x^2 + 2x$

1) Take out the biggest number that goes into every term:      2

2) Take out any letter that is in every term (to its highest power):      $x$

3) Open the brackets and work out what needs to go inside:      $2x(2x + 2)$

4) Check whether you're right by multiplying out the brackets:

$$2x(2x + 2) = 4x^2 + 2x$$

**Q4**    Simplify the following expressions.

**a)** $b \times b \times b \times b \times b =$ ............

**b)** $c \times d \times 4 =$ ............

**c)** $2e \times 6f =$ ............

**d)** $5g \times 3g^2 =$ ............

**e)** $7h^2 \times 8 =$ ............

**f)** $2j^2 \times j \times k =$ ............

**Q5**    Factorise the expressions below. Each has <u>4</u> as a common factor.

**a)** $4x + 8 =$ ............

**b)** $12 - 8x =$ ............

**c)** $4 - 16x =$ ............

**d)** $4x^2 + 64 =$ ............

**Q6**    Factorise the expressions below. Each has <u>x</u> as a common factor.

**a)** $2x + x^2 =$ ............

**b)** $2x - x^2 =$ ............

**c)** $x - 16x^2 =$ ............

**d)** $4x^2 - 3x =$ ............

**Q7**    Factorise the expressions below by taking out any <u>common factors</u>.

**a)** $2x + 4 =$ ............

**b)** $3x + 12 =$ ............

**c)** $24 + 12x =$ ............

**d)** $16x + 4y =$ ............

**e)** $3x + 15 =$ ............

**f)** $30 + 10x =$ ............

**g)** $9x^2 + 3x =$ ............

**h)** $5x^2 + 10x =$ ............

**i)** $7x^2 + 21x =$ ............

**j)** $3y + xy^2 =$ ............

First look for any numbers the terms have in common, then look for the letters.

# Solving Equations

**Q1** Solve these equations:

**a)** $a + 6 = 20$

.....................

**b)** $b + 12 = 30$

.....................

**c)** $48 + c = 77$

.....................

**d)** $397 + d = 842$

.....................

**e)** $e + 9.8 = -14.1$

.....................

**f)** $3 + f = -7$

.....................

**Q2** Solve these equations:

**a)** $g - 7 = 4$

.....................

**b)** $h - 14 = 11$

.....................

**c)** $i - 38 = 46$

.....................

**d)** $j - 647 = 353$

.....................

**e)** $k - 6.4 = 2.9$

.....................

**f)** $l^2 - 8 = -4$

.....................

**Q3** Solve these equations:

**a)** $4m = 28$

.....................

**b)** $7n = 84$

.....................

**c)** $15p = 645$

.....................

**d)** $279q = 1395$

.....................

**e)** $6.4r = -9.6$

.....................

**f)** $5s^2 = 80$

.....................

**Q4** Solve these equations:

**a)** $3x + 2 = 14$ .....................

**b)** $5x - 4 = 31$ .....................

**c)** $8 + 6x = 50$ .....................

**d)** $20 - 2x^3 = -108$ .....................

**Q5** Solve these equations:

**a)** $\frac{x}{3} + 4 = 10$

.....................

**b)** $\frac{x}{5} - 9 = 6$

.....................

**c)** $4 + \frac{x}{9} = 6$

.....................

**d)** $\frac{x}{17} - 11 = 31$

.....................

# Using Formulas

**Q1**   $m = 5n + 2p$.  Find the value of $m$ when $n = 3$ and $p = 4$.   ................................

**Q2**   $c = 8d - 4e$.  Find the value of $c$ when $d = 6$ and $e = 2$.   ................................

**Q3**   $f = \dfrac{9g}{2h}$.  Find the value of $f$ when $g = 6$ and $h = 2$.   ................................

**Q4**   A chair manufacturing company uses the following formula to work out their profit:
$$P = 3a - 2000$$
$P$ is their profit in pounds and $a$ is the number of chairs sold.

**a)** What is the profit when 1500 chairs are sold?   ...................................

**b)** Do they make a profit if they only sell 700 chairs?   ...................................

**Q5**   The cost of framing a picture, $C$ pence, depends on the <u>dimensions of the picture</u>. If $C = 10L + 5W$, where $L$ is the length in cm and $W$ is the width in cm, then find the cost of framing:

**a)** a picture of length 40 cm and width 24 cm   ...................................

**b)** a square picture of sides 30 cm.   ...................................

**Q6**   To work out the number of sheep to put in each of his fields, a farmer uses the formula:

$$\text{number of sheep in each field} = \frac{\text{total number of sheep} - 8}{\text{number of fields available}}$$

Find the number of sheep the farmer should put in each field if:

**a)** there are 5 fields available and 243 sheep   ...................................

**b)** there are 7 fields available and 582 sheep   ...................................

**Q7**   A baker uses the following formula to work out how long to bake her cakes for:

$$\text{number of minutes} = \frac{\text{surface area of cake (cm}^2\text{)} \times \text{oven temperature (}^\circ\text{C)}}{300}$$

Find the number of minutes that the baker should bake a cake for if it has a surface area of 50 cm² and the oven is at a temperature of 180 °C.

................................

# Making Formulas From Words

It's no big mystery — algebra is just like normal sums, but with the odd letter or two stuck in for good measure.

**Q1**  Write the algebraic expression for these:

a) Three more than $x$ .............................

b) Seven less than $y$ ...........................

c) Four multiplied by $x$ .........................

d) $y$ multiplied by $y$ ...........................

e) Ten divided by $b$ ...........................

f) A number add five ...........................

**Q2**  Steven is 16 years old. How old will he be in:

a) 5 years? .........................

b) 10 years? .........................

c) $x$ years? .........................

**Q3**  Tickets for a football match cost £25 each. What is the cost for:

a) 2 tickets? ....................

b) 6 tickets? ....................

c) $y$ tickets? ....................

CGP Wanderers Football Club

Vs. United Rovers FC

Comfy Seat
East stand lower bit
Row 20
Seat 104

£25.00

**Q4**  There are $n$ books in a pile. Write an expression for the number of books in a pile that has:

a) 3 more books ....................

b) 4 fewer books ....................

c) Twice as many books ....................

**Q5**  a) This square has sides of length 3 cm.

What is its perimeter? ....................

What is its area? ....................

b) This square has sides of length $d$ cm.

What is its perimeter? ....................

What is its area? ....................

3 cm

3 cm

$d$ cm

$d$ cm

**Q6**  A cube has sides of length $x$ cm. What is its volume? ........................................

**Q7**  The cost ($C$) of hiring a mountain bike is £10, plus £5 for each hour you use the bike ($h$). Write down a formula that can be used for working out the cost of hiring a bike.

..........................................................................................

# Rearranging Formulas

Rearranging is getting the letter you want out of the
formula and making it the subject.

Example:- Rearrange the formula $p = 3q + r$ to make $q$ the subject.

$p = 3q + r$

$p - r = 3q$

$\dfrac{p - r}{3} = q$

$q = \dfrac{p - r}{3}$

Subtract $r$ from each side

Divide by 3

Rewrite starting with new subject

**Remember**
The same method applies
to rearranging formulas
as to solving equations.

**Q1**  Rearrange the following formulas to make the <u>letter in brackets</u> the new subject:

**a)** $y = x + 4$   $(x)$

**d)** $a = 7b + 10$   $(b)$

**g)** $y = 3x + \frac{1}{2}$   $(x)$

......................

......................

......................

**b)** $y = 2x + 3$   $(x)$

**e)** $w = 14 + 2z$   $(z)$

**h)** $y = 3 - x$   $(x)$

......................

......................

......................

**c)** $y = 4x - 5$   $(x)$

**f)** $s = 4t - 3$   $(t)$

**i)** $y = 5(x + 2)$   $(x)$

......................

......................

......................

**Q2**  Rearrange the following, to make the <u>letter in brackets</u> the subject of the formulas:

**a)** $y = \dfrac{x}{10}$ $(x)$ ......................

**e)** $f = \dfrac{3g}{8}$   $(g)$ ......................

**b)** $s = \dfrac{t}{14}$ $(t)$ ......................

**f)** $y = \dfrac{x}{5} + 1$   $(x)$ ......................

**c)** $a = \dfrac{2b}{3}$ $(b)$ ......................

**g)** $y = \dfrac{x}{2} - 3$   $(x)$ ......................

**d)** $d = \dfrac{3e}{4}$ $(e)$ ......................

**h)** $a = \dfrac{b}{3} - 5$   $(b)$ ......................

**Q3**  The cost ($c$) of a taxi journey is £1.40 per mile ($m$), plus an extra charge of £1.50.

**a)** Write down a formula with $c$ as the subject.   ......................

**b)** Rearrange this to make $m$ the subject.   ......................

**c)** Frank wants to know how far his hotel is from the airport.  He knows the taxi
fare from one to the other is £9.90.  How far is the hotel from the airport? ......................

**Q4**  Florence booked 5 tickets for a concert.  Each ticket cost £18.50 plus a booking fee.
There was also a fee of £5 added to the order to cover postage.
The total amount Florence paid was £116.
Work out the booking fee for each ticket.

......................

# Number Patterns and Sequences

**Q1**   Draw the next two pictures in each pattern.
How many match sticks are used in each picture?

**a)**

,

....... ....... ....... ....... .......

**b)**

, , ,

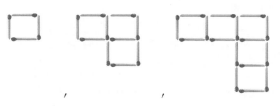

Look for patterns in the numbers as well as pictures.

....... ....... .......

,

....... .......

**c)**

, , , ,

....... ....... ....... ....... .......

**Q2**   Look for the pattern and then fill in the next three lines.  Some of the answers are too big to fit on a calculator display so you must spot the pattern.

**a)**

| $7 \times 6$ | $= 42$ |
| $67 \times 66$ | $= 4422$ |
| $667 \times 666$ | $= 444\ 222$ |
| $6667 \times 6666$ | $= $ .......................... |
| $66\ 667 \times 66\ 666$ | $= $ .......................... |
| $666\ 667 \times 666\ 666$ | $= $ .......................... |

**b)**

$1 \times 81 = 81$

$21 \times 81 = 1701$

$321 \times 81 = 26\ 001$

$4321 \times 81 = 350\ 001$

$54\ 321 \times 81 = $ ........................

$654\ 321 \times 81 = $ ........................

$7\ 654\ 321 \times 81 = $ ........................

**Q3**   The first five terms of a sequence are 3, 7, 11, 15, 19...
Is 34 a term in the sequence?  Explain your answer.

.............................................................................................................

# Number Patterns and Sequences

Once you've worked out the next numbers, go back and write down exactly what you did — that will be the rule you're after.

**Q4** In each of the questions below, write down the next three numbers in the sequence and write the rule that you used.

**a)** 1, 3, 5, 7, ........., ........., ......... Rule ........................................................

**b)** 2, 4, 8, 16, ........., ........., ......... Rule ........................................................

**c)** 3, 30, 300, 3000, ........., ........., ......... Rule ..............................................

**d)** 3, 7, 11, 15, ........., ........., ......... Rule ....................................................

**Q5** The letter $n$ describes the position of a term in the sequence. For example, if $n = 1$, that's the 1st term...if $n = 10$ that's the 10th term and so on. In the following, use the rule given to generate (or make) the first 5 terms.

**a)** $3n + 1$ so if $n = 1$ the 1st term is **$(3 \times 1) + 1 = 4$**

   $n = 2$ the 2nd term is ......................................... = .............

   $n = 3$ ......................................... = .............

   $n = 4$ ......................................... = .............

**b)** $5n - 2$, when $n = 1, 2, 3, 4$ and 5
   produces the sequence ........., ........., ........., ........., .........

**c)** $n^2$, when $n = 1, 2, 3, 4$, and 5
   produces the sequence ........., ........., ........., ........., .........

**Q6** Write down an expression for the $n^{th}$ term of the following sequences:

**a)** 2, 4, 6, 8, ...
   ........................................................

**b)** 1, 3, 5, 7, ...
   ........................................................

The common difference tells you what multiple of n to use in the expression.

**c)** 5, 8, 11, 14, ...
   ........................................................

**Q7** Mike has opened a bank account to save for a holiday. He opened the account with £20 and puts £15 into the account at the end of each week. So at the end of the first week the balance of the account is £35. What will the balance of the account be after:

a) 3 weeks? ............................    **b)** 5 weeks? ...............................

c) Write down an expression that will let Mike work out how much he'll have in his account after any number of weeks he chooses.

   ...............................................

d) What will the balance of the account be after 18 weeks?

   ...............................................

# Trial and Improvement

**Q1** Use the trial and improvement method to solve the equation $x^3 = 50$.
Give your answer to one decimal place. Two trials have been done for you.

Try $x = 3$  $x^3 = 27$  (too small)
Try $x = 4$  $x^3 = 64$  (too big)

..............................................

**Q2** Use the trial and improvement method to solve these equations.
Give your answers to one decimal place.

**a)** $x^2 + x = 80$

..............................................

**b)** $x^3 - x = 100$

..............................................

**Show all the numbers you've tried, not just your final answer...
or you'll be chucking away easy marks.**

# Inequalities

Yet another one of those bits of Maths that looks worse than it is —
these are just like equations, really, except for the symbols.

## The 4 Inequality Symbols:

> means greater than          < means less than
≥ means greater than or equal to          ≤ means less than or equal to

Inequalities can be represented on number lines.  You need to know this notation, too:

Eg

```
    -4  -3  -2  -1   0   1   2   3   4
```

**REMEMBER:**
● includes the value
○ does not include it

represents the inequality −3 ≤ x < 2

**Q1**    Write down an inequality for each of the diagrams below.

a)
```
   -1  0   1   2   3   4   5
```
....................

g)
```
   -3  -2  -1   0   1   2   3
```
....................

b)
```
   -2  -1   0   1   2   3   4
```
....................

h)
```
  -17 -16 -15 -14 -13 -12 -11
```
....................

c)
```
    8   9  10  11  12  13  14
```
....................

i)
```
   20  21  22  23  24  25  26
```
....................

d)
```
   -4  -3  -2  -1   0   1   2
```
....................

j)
```
   -2  -1   0   1   2   3   4
```
....................

e)
```
   -7  -6  -5  -4  -3  -2  -1
```
....................

k)
```
   -1   0   1   2   3   4   5
```
....................

f)
```
    0   1   2   3   4   5   6
```
....................

l)
```
   -3  -2  -1   0   1   2   3
```
....................

**Q2**    Solve the following inequalities:

a) $2x \geq 16$    ....................

e) $10x > -2$    ....................

i) $5x + 4 < 24$    ....................

b) $4x > -20$    ....................

f) $5 + x \geq 12$    ....................

j) $5x + 7 \leq 32$    ....................

c) $x + 2 > 5$    ....................

g) $x/4 > 10$    ....................

k) $3x + 12 \leq 30$    ....................

d) $x - 3 \leq 10$    ....................

h) $x/3 \leq 1$    ....................

l) $2x - 7 \geq 8$    ....................

**Q3**    There are <u>1130</u> pupils in a school and no classes have more than <u>32</u> pupils.  What is the least number of <u>classrooms</u> that could be used?  Show this information as an inequality.

*Call the number of classrooms x.*

....................................

**Q4**    Jon has a budget of £10 to buy food for his dinner.  He picks up a steak which costs £4.70 and a tin of sweetcorn which costs 90p.  Potatoes cost 65p each.
What is the greatest number of potatoes Jon can buy with the money he has left?

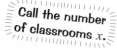

....................................

# Simultaneous Equations with Graphs

## The solution of two simultaneous equations is simply the $x$ and $y$ values where their graphs cross

1) Simultaneous equations can be plotted as two <u>straight-line graphs</u> on the <u>same axes</u>.

2) The point where the lines cross will have <u>coordinates</u> equal to the <u>values of $x$ and $y$</u> which satisfy both equations.

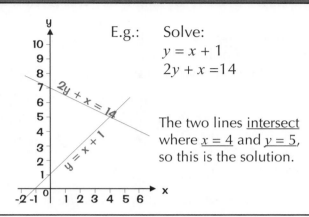

E.g.: Solve:
$$y = x + 1$$
$$2y + x = 14$$

The two lines <u>intersect</u> where <u>$x = 4$</u> and <u>$y = 5$</u>, so this is the solution.

**Q1** Solve these simultaneous equations by looking at the graphs.
Then check your answers by substituting the values back into the equations.

**a)** $y + 2x = 9$
$3y = x + 6$

Solution:
$x = $ .........., $y = $ ..........

**b)** $y = x + 6$
$3y + x = 18$

Solution:
$x = $ .........., $y = $ ..........

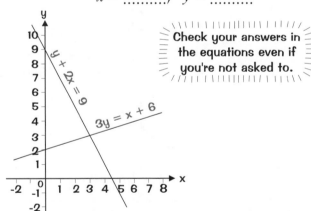

*Check your answers in the equations even if you're not asked to.*

**Q2** For the pair of simultaneous equations below:

**a)** draw and label a pair of axes with $x$ from –3 to 7, and $y$ from –6 to 6
**b)** complete the <u>two tables of values</u>
**c)** plot <u>two straight-line graphs</u> onto your axes, remembering to label each graph
**d)** use your graphs to find the values of <u>$x$</u> and <u>$y$</u> satisfying both equations
**e)** check your answers by <u>substituting</u> them into both of the equations.

$y = x + 2$
$y = 3x - 2$

| x | –2 | 0 | 4 |
|---|---|---|---|
| y = x+2 | 0 | 2 | |

| x | 0 | 1 | 2 |
|---|---|---|---|
| y = 3x–2 | –2 | | |

$x = $ ..................

$y = $ ..................

## X and Y Coordinates

Remember — 1)    x comes before y

          2)    x goes a-cross (get it) the page. (Ah, the old ones are the best...)

**Q1**    On the grid plot the following points.
Label the points A, B…
Join the points with straight lines as you plot them.

A(0, 8)      B(4, 6)      C(4.5, 6.5)      D(5, 6)
E(9, 8)      F(8, 5.5)      G(5, 5)      H(8, 4)
I(7.5, 2)      J(6, 2)      K(5, 4)      L(4.5, 3.5)
M(4, 4)      N(3, 2)      O(1.5, 2)      P(1, 4)
Q(4, 5)      R(1, 5.5)      S(0, 8).

You should see the outline of an insect.

What is it? .............................

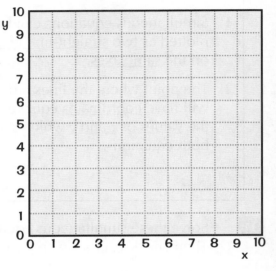

**Q2**    The map shows the island of Tenerife where the sun never stops shining...

**a)** Use the map to write
down the coordinates
of the following:

Airport ( .... , .... )

Mount Teide ( .... , .... )

Santa Cruz ( .... , .... )

Puerto Colon ( .... , .... )

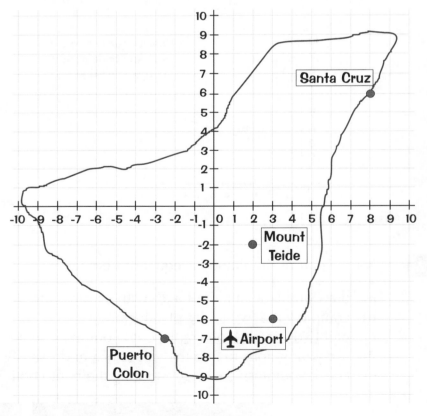

**b)** Use the coordinates given to mark the following holiday destinations on the map.
Las Americas (-4, -6), El Medano (4, -4), Icod (-6, 2), Laguna (3, 7), Taganana (9, 9)

**c)** The cable car takes you to the top of Mount Teide. It starts at (3, 1) and ends at (2, -2).
Draw the cable car route on the map.

# Midpoint of a Line Segment

**Q1**   Find the midpoint of the line segments AB, where A and B have coordinates:

**a)** A(2, 3)   B(4, 5)   ....................

**d)** A(3, 15)   B(13, 3)   ....................

**b)** A(1, 8)   B(9, 2)   ....................

**e)** A(6, 6)   B(0, 0)   ....................

**c)** A(0, 11)   B(12, 11)   ....................

**f)** A(15, 9)   B(3, 3)   ....................

**Your answers should be coordinates too.**

ahh... nice'n'easy...

**Q2**   Find the midpoints of each of these line segments:

**a)** Line segment PQ, where P has coordinates (1, 5) and Q has coordinates (5, 6).   .............................................

**b)** Line segment AB, where A has coordinates (3, 3) and B has coordinates (4, 0).   .............................................

**c)** Line segment RS, where R has coordinates (4, 5) and S has coordinates (0, 0).   .............................................

**d)** Line segment PQ, where P has coordinates (1, 3) and Q has coordinates (3, 1).   .............................................

**e)** Line segment GH, where G has coordinates (0, 0) and H has coordinates (–6, –7).   .............................................

**Q3**   A college wants to install drinking water fountains at convenient locations around the college site.  The fountains are to be placed at points exactly halfway between the main buildings (shown below on the coordinate map).

**a)** Where should they be placed between the following buildings?  Give the coordinates.

Art and Biology:   ....................

Gym and Humanities:   ....................

Languages and Maths:   ....................

**b)** What building is halfway between Physics and the Finance Office? Give the name and coordinates.

....................................................

*SECTION THREE — GRAPHS*

# Straight-Line Graphs

The <u>very first thing</u> you've got to do is work out a <u>table of values</u>.

Example: Draw the graph of $y = 3x - 1$ for values of $x$ between 0 and 4.

1) First complete a <u>table of values:</u>

| x | 0 | 1 | 2 | 3 | 4 |
|---|---|---|---|---|---|
| y | -1 | 2 | 5 | 8 | 11 |

← decided by the question

← worked out using y = 3x - 1

2) Draw the axes.
3) Plot the points.
4) Draw a straight line through the points.

**Q1** On the grid shown, draw axes with $x$ from 0 to 8 and $y$ from 0 to 14.

**Q2 a)** Complete the table of values, for $y = x + 2$.

| x | 0 | 1 | 2 | 3 | 4 | 5 | 6 |
|---|---|---|---|---|---|---|---|
| y | 2 | | | 5 | | | |

**b)** Use your <u>table of values</u> to draw the graph of $y = x + 2$ on the grid opposite.

**Q3 a)** Fill in the table of values for $y + x = 8$.

| x | 0 | 1 | 2 | 3 | 4 | 5 | 6 |
|---|---|---|---|---|---|---|---|
| y | | | | | | | |

**b)** Draw the graph of $y + x = 8$ on the grid opposite.

**Q4** A rough way of changing temperatures from Celsius to Fahrenheit is to 'double it and add 30' ($y = 2x + 30$).

**a)** Fill in the table below to change the temperatures in Celsius ($x$) to Fahrenheit ($y$).

| x | 0 | 5 | 10 | 15 | 20 | 25 | 30 |
|---|---|---|---|---|---|---|---|
| y | 30 | | | | 70 | | |

**b)** Use your <u>table of values</u> to draw a temperature conversion graph. Draw and label the axes with $x$ from 0 to 30, and $y$ from 0 to 100.

# Straight-Line Graphs

☞ Now it's time to find the gradient of a line and its equation — follow these steps...

> **STEP 1:** Work out the gradient of the line, call this '$m$'.
>
> **STEP 2:** Find where the graph crosses the $y$-axis, call this '$c$',
>
> **STEP 3:** Put your values into the formula $y = mx + c$ — and that's it!

**Q5**    Find the gradient of:

a) line A ......................

b) line B ......................

c) line C ......................

d) line D ......................

e) line E ......................

f) line F ......................

g) line G ......................

h) line H ......................

i) line I ......................

j) line J ......................

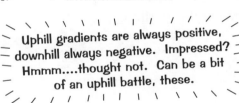
Uphill gradients are always positive, downhill always negative. Impressed? Hmmm....thought not. Can be a bit of an uphill battle, these.

**Q6**    For each of these lines, find the gradient, $m$, and the $y$-intercept, $c$.
Hence write down the <u>equation</u> of the line.

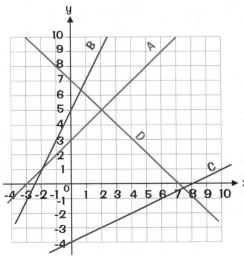

Line A:

$m =$ ............, $c =$ ............

equation is ......................

Line B:

$m =$ ............, $c =$ ............

equation is ......................

Line C:

$m =$ ............, $c =$ ............

equation is ......................

Line D:

$m =$ ............, $c =$ ............

equation is ......................

**Q7**    Which of the following equations are straight lines?

a) $y = 4x + 6$         b) $y = 6x - 3$         c) $3y = x^2 + 2$         d) $2y = 4 - 5x$

# Straight-Line Graphs

The equations of straight-line graphs can be written in the form:

$$y = mx + c$$

| The number multiplying the x term tells you the <u>gradient</u> of the graph. | The number by itself tells you where the graph crosses the y axis. This is the <u>y-intercept</u>. |

**Q8** Using $y = mx + c$, draw these graphs on the axes opposite.

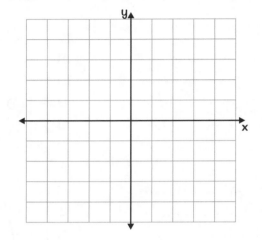

**a)** $y = x + 2$

**b)** $y = 2x + 1$

**c)** $y = 1 - 2x$

**d)** $y = 3x - 2$

**Q9** The following are equations of linear graphs. <u>Without plotting</u> the graphs, state the <u>gradient</u> of each graph and the coordinates of the <u>y-intercept</u>.

**a)** $y = 4x + 2$   .................................

**b)** $y = 5x - 1$   .................................

**c)** $y = 6x$   .................................

**d)** $y = 5 + 2x$   .................................

**e)** $y = x$   .................................

**f)** $y = 3 - x$   .................................

**g)** $y + 2x = 10$   .................................

**h)** $2y = x + 4$   .................................

**Q10** Find the values for $m$ and $c$ if the linear graph $y = mx + c$ has a gradient of 3 and passes through (0, 8).

...................................................................................................................

**Q11** Two paving companies want to add equations to their website so customers can estimate the cost of paving their driveway by typing in a few numbers. The equation should use the letters $y$ for the total cost, and $x$ for the size of the driveway, and be in the form $y = mx + c$. The two companies charge the following:
Company A = a flat rate of £500, plus £70 per m² of driveway to be paved.
Company B = a flat rate of £700, plus £50 per m² of driveway to be paved.

**a)** Write an equation for each company showing the total cost of paving a driveway.
A ...................................................... B ......................................................

**b)** Joe's driveway is 50 m². Which company would be cheapest for Joe? ..............

# Travel Graphs

**Q1** The graph shows Nicola's car journey from her house to Alan's house and back, picking up Robbie on the way.

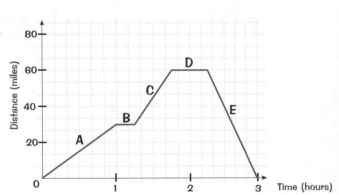

**a)** If Nicola started her trip at 10.00 am at what time did she return home? ....................

**b)** How far is Robbie's house from Nicola's? ....................

**c)** How long did they stop at Alan's for? ....................

**d)** During which section was the speed greatest? ....................

**e)** How long did the return journey take? ....................

**f)** What was the speed of the car during section E? ....................

> You can work out where the houses are by looking for the flat parts of the graph — the bits where Nicola stops.

**Q2** Marcus competes in a 10 km race. All the runners are given a small device to wear which records the time as they pass through certain checkpoints. Later, Marcus gets a graph of his performance during the race, shown below.

**a)** Between what times was Marcus running the fastest?

...................................................

**b)** Calculate his fastest speed in km/hr.

...................................................

**c)** What time did Marcus stop for a drink?

...................................................

**d)** For how long did he stop?

...................................................

> **Remember:**
> Average speed = $\dfrac{\text{total dist. travelled}}{\text{total time taken}}$

**e)** How long did it take Marcus to complete the 10 km run (in hours)? ...................................................

**f)** What was the average speed for his entire run? ...................................................

# Conversion Graphs and Real-Life Graphs

**Q1** This graph can be used to convert the distance (miles) travelled in a taxi to the fare payable (£). How much will the fare be if you travel:

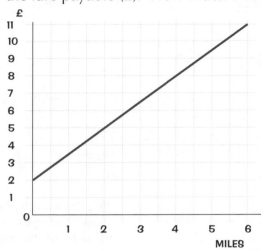

**a)** 2 miles ....................

**b)** 5 miles ....................

**c)** 10 miles ....................

**d)** Mike lives 4.5 miles away from his friend. Is £16 enough money for Mike to get a taxi to his friend's house and back?

.....................

**Q2** 80 km is roughly equal to 50 miles. Use this information to draw a conversion graph on the grid. Use the graph to estimate the number of miles equal to:

**a)** 20 km ....................

**b)** 70 km ....................

**c)** 90 km ....................

**Q3** How many km are equal to:

**a)** 40 miles ....................

**b)** 10 miles ....................

**c)** 30 miles ....................

**Q4** The graph below shows the costs for hiring a holiday cottage for one week.

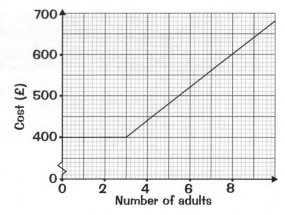

**a)** How many adults are included in the basic weekly cost?

.....................

**b)** Estimate the cost per adult for additional adults.

.....................

# Quadratic Graphs

If an expression has an $x^2$ term in it, it's quadratic. The graphs you get from quadratic expressions are always curves with a certain shape...

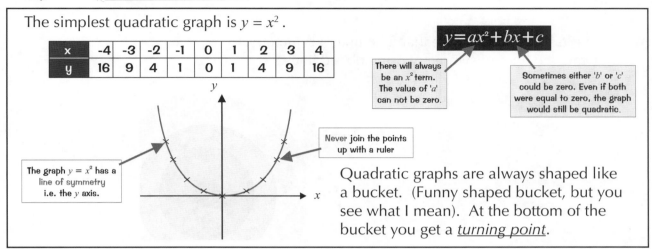

The simplest quadratic graph is $y = x^2$.

| x | -4 | -3 | -2 | -1 | 0 | 1 | 2 | 3 | 4 |
|---|----|----|----|----|---|---|---|---|---|
| y | 16 | 9 | 4 | 1 | 0 | 1 | 4 | 9 | 16 |

$$y = ax^2 + bx + c$$

There will always be an $x^2$ term. The value of '$a$' can not be zero.

Sometimes either '$b$' or '$c$' could be zero. Even if both were equal to zero, the graph would still be quadratic.

Never join the points up with a ruler

The graph $y = x^2$ has a line of symmetry i.e. the $y$ axis.

Quadratic graphs are always shaped like a bucket. (Funny shaped bucket, but you see what I mean). At the bottom of the bucket you get a _turning point_.

**Q1 a)** Complete this table of values for the graph $y = x^2 - 4x + 1$.

**b)** Plot the graph $y = x^2 - 4x + 1$, using axes with $x$ from -2 to 5 and $y$ from -3 to 13.

| x | -2 | -1 | 0 | 1 | 2 | 3 | 4 |
|---|----|----|---|---|---|---|---|
| $x^2$ | 4 | 1 | | | | 9 | |
| -4x | 8 | | | | | -12 | |
| 1 | 1 | 1 | | | | 1 | |
| $y = x^2 - 4x + 1$ | 13 | 6 | | | | -2 | |

**c)** Draw and label the <u>line of symmetry</u>.

**d)** Use your graph to find approximate solutions of the equation $x^2 - 4x + 1 = 0$.

$x = $ ........ or ........

**Q2 a)** Complete this table of values for the graph $y = 3 - x^2$.

| x | -4 | -3 | -2 | -1 | 0 | 1 | 2 | 3 | 4 |
|---|----|----|----|----|---|---|---|---|---|
| 3 | 3 | 3 | 3 | 3 | 3 | 3 | 3 | 3 | 3 |
| $-x^2$ | -16 | | | | | | -4 | | |
| $y = 3 - x^2$ | -13 | | | | | | -1 | | |

**b)** Draw the graph $y = 3 - x^2$ for $x$ from -4 to 4.

**c)** Use your graph to find approximate solutions of the equation $3 - x^2 = 0$.

$x = $ ........ or ........

**Q3 a)** Draw the graph $y = -x^2 + x + 4$ for values of $x$ from -3 to 4.
**b)** Use your graph to find approximate solutions to the equation $-x^2 + x + 4 = 0$

$x = $ .......... or ..........

If any points look a bit strange, check you've got them right in the <u>table of values</u>. I know it's boring doing it all again, but it shouldn't be too hard if you've put all the steps in. And it'll mean you <u>don't get it wrong</u>. Which is always nice.

# Symmetry

To work out if you've got a line of symmetry, just imagine you're folding the shape in half. If the sides will fold exactly together, then hey presto, it's symmetrical about the fold.

**Q1** These shapes have more than one line of symmetry.
Draw the lines of symmetry using dotted lines.

a)

b)

c)

**Q2** Some of the letters of the alphabet have lines of symmetry.
Draw the lines of symmetry using dotted lines.

## A B C D E F G H I J K L M

## N O P Q R S T U V W X Y Z

**Q3** Write down the order of rotational symmetry of each of the following shapes:

a)

square

..............................

b)

rectangle

..............................

c)

equilateral triangle

..............................

d)

parallelogram

..............................

# Symmetry

**Q4** Complete the following diagrams so that they have rotational symmetry about centre C of the order stated:

**a)**     order 2

**b)**     order 4

**c)**     order 3

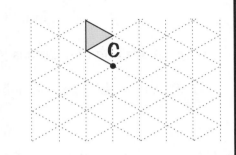

**Q5** Shade six more squares to complete a pattern with four lines of symmetry.

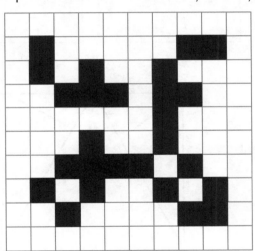

**Q6** Draw the line of symmetry on this shape:

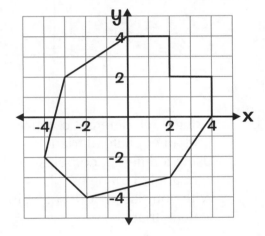

**Q7** Here is a cuboid:

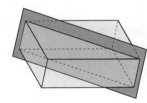

Is the plane a plane of symmetry?

**Q8** How many planes of symmetry does this <u>triangular prism</u> have?

**Q9** In the square-based pyramid shown, is this a plane of symmetry?

# Properties of 2D Shapes

**Q1**   Fill in the gaps in these sentences.

a) An isosceles triangle has ........ equal sides and ........ equal angles.

b) A triangle with all its sides equal and all its angles equal is called an
...................... triangle.

c) A scalene triangle has ........ equal sides and ........ equal angles.

d) A triangle with one right-angle is called a ........................................ triangle.

**Q2**   By joining dots, draw four different isosceles triangles — one in each box.

**Q3**   Using three different coloured pencils:
Find an equilateral triangle and shade it in.
Using a different colour, shade in two different
right angled triangles.
With your last colour shade in two different
scalene triangles.

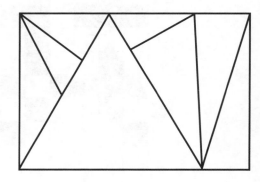

**Q4**   How many triangles are there in this diagram?

..........................

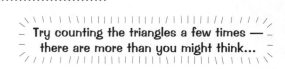
Try counting the triangles a few times —
there are more than you might think...

What sort of triangles are they?

..........................

There are only 4 types of triangle, so make sure you know them all —
think of all those nice fat juicy marks...

*SECTION FOUR — SHAPES AND AREA*

# Properties of 2D Shapes

Here's a few easy marks for you —
all you've got to do is remember the shapes
and a few facts about them... it's a waste
of marks not to bother.

**Q5** Fill in the blanks in the table.

| NAME | DRAWING | DESCRIPTION |
|---|---|---|
| Square | | Sides of equal length.<br>Opposite sides parallel.<br>Four right angles. |
| ............. | ................................. | Opposite sides parallel and the same length.  Four right angles. |
| ............. | | Opposite sides are ...................<br>and equal.<br>Opposite angles are equal. |
| Trapezium | | Only ..........<br>sides are parallel. |
| Rhombus | | A parallelogram but with all sides ................ |
| Kite | ................................. | Two pairs of adjacent equal sides. |

**Q6** Stephen is measuring the angles inside a parallelogram for his maths homework.
To save time, he measures just one and works out what the other angles must
be from this.  If the angle he measures is 52°, what are the other three?

.........., .........., ..........,

54

# Congruence and Similarity

For the following sets of shapes, underline the one which is <u>not</u> congruent to the others.

**Q1**  a)  b)  c)  d)

**Q2**  a)  b)  c)  d)

**Q3** Two picture frames are shown. One picture is <u>similar</u> to the other. Calculate L cm, the length of the smaller frame.

.................................................................

**Q4** For each of the following pairs, say with a reason whether the shapes are similar.

a)

b)

.........................................    ...............................................

**Q5** Angle ABC = Angle PQR and Angle BCA = Angle QRP

Are the triangles similar? ................

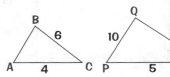

**Q6** Which of the following must be <u>similar</u> to each other? ...............................

   **A** Two circles    **C** Two rectangles    **E** Two equilateral triangles
   **B** Two rhombuses    **D** Two squares    **F** Two isosceles triangles

*SECTION FOUR — SHAPES AND AREA*

# 3D Shapes and Projections

**Q1** What are the names of these shapes?

**a)**

..........................

**b)**

..........................

**c)**

..........................

**d)**

..........................

**e)**

..........................

**f)**

..........................

**g)**

..........................

**Q2** This shape is not drawn to scale.
Draw an isometric projection of it
on the grid opposite.

**Q3** The diagram shows an isometric projection of a triangular prism.

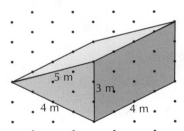

**a)** Draw the front elevation, side elevation and plan view.

**b)** How many faces does this prism have? ................

**c)** How many edges does this prism have? ................

**d)** How many vertices does this prism have? ................

**Q4** Use the front, side and plan views of this
object to sketch it in 3D.

Front

Side

Plan

# Perimeters

**Q1** Work out the perimeters of the following shapes :

**a)**

Rectangle Perimeter =

$(2 \times \underline{\ \ \ \ }) + (2 \times \underline{\ \ \ \ }) = \underline{\ \ \ \ \ \ }$ m

**b)**

Triangle Perimeter = ...... + ...... + ......

= ......... cm

**c)**

Symmetrical Five Sided Shape

Perimeter = ..... + ..... + ..... + ..... + .....

= ....... cm

**Q2** A square garden has sides of length 10 m.
How much fencing is needed to go around it? ......................................................... m

**Q3** Find the perimeter of these shapes (you may need to work out some of the lengths):

**a)**

Perimeter .......................................

**b)**

Perimeter .......................................

**Q4** Isaac is putting a paper border across all of his living room walls.
He has made a plan of the room with dimensions, shown here.

**a)** What is the total length of border he
would need to go around the whole room?

.......................................................

**b)** The border comes in rolls of 5 m.
How many would Isaac need to buy for his room?

.....................................................................

---

*SECTION FOUR — SHAPES AND AREA*

# Areas

For rectangles and squares, working out the area is a piece of pie — it's just **LENGTH TIMES WIDTH**. Nowt more to it.

## Area of a Rectangle = Length × Width

**Q1** Calculate the areas of the following rectangles:

**a)** Length = 10 cm,  Width = 4 cm,   Area = ..... × ..... = ........ cm².

**b)** Length = 55 cm,  Width = 19 cm,  Area = ................................... cm².

**c)** Length = 155 m,  Width = 28 m,   Area = ................................... m².

**d)** Length = 3.7 km, Width = 1.5 km,  Area = ................................... km².

**Q2** Measure the lengths and widths of each of these rectangles, then calculate the area.

**a)**

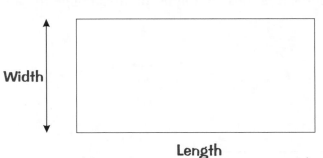

Width = ............ cm

Length = ............ cm

Area = ............ cm²

**b)**

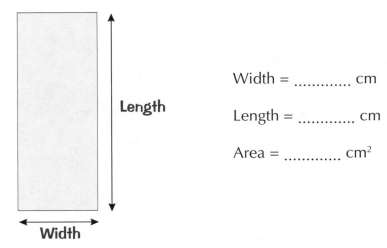

Width = ............ cm

Length = ............ cm

Area = ............ cm²

**Q3** Sabrina is buying carpet for two rectangular rooms in her house.
One room is 4.8 m long and 3.9 m wide.
The other room is 4.2 m long and 3.1 m wide.
How many square metres of carpet does she need to buy?

...............................................

# Areas

➤ Triangles aren't much harder, but <u>remember</u> to TIMES BY THE ½.

## Area of a Triangle = ½ (Base × Height)

**Q4**    Calculate the areas of the following triangles:

**a)** Base = 12 cm,  Height = 9 cm,   Area = ½ ( ...... × ...... ) = ...... cm².

**b)** Base = 5 cm,  Height = 3 cm,   Area = ................................. cm².

**c)** Base = 25 m,  Height = 7 m,   Area = ................................. m².

**d)** Base = 1.6 m,  Height = 6.4 m,   Area = ................................. m².

**e)** Base = 700 cm,  Height = 350 cm,   Area = ................................. cm².

**Q5**    Measure the base and height of each of these triangles, then calculate the area.

**a)**

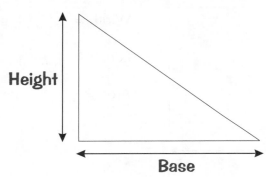

Height = ............ cm

Base = ............ cm

Area = ............ cm²

**b)**

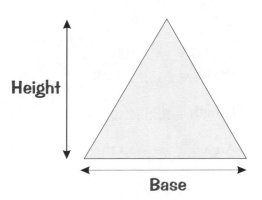

Height = ............ cm

Base = ............ cm

Area = ............ cm²

**Q6**    Peter is making a kite.  He has made a frame from wooden poles.
What is the minimum area of fabric he needs to buy to cover the kite?

15 cm

15 cm | 15 cm

35 cm

.................................................................................

Think of the fabric he needs as four
right-angled triangles sewn together.

# Areas

Bit more tricky, these... but look — they're all just rectangles and triangles.
Work out each bit separately, then add the areas together — easy.

**Q7** Calculate the areas of these composite shapes...

**a)**

Shape A: length = ........ width = ........

Area = ........ × ........ = ........cm²

Shape B: length = ........ width = ........

Area = ........ × ........ = ........ cm²

Total (area A + area B) = ........ + ........ = ........ cm²

**b)** Shape A (rectangle): ........ × ........ = ........ cm²

Shape B (triangle): ½ (base x height)

Base = ........ cm , Height = ........ cm

Area = ½ ( ........ × ........ ) = ........ cm²

Total Area = ........ + ........ = ........ cm²

**c)**

Shape A (rectangle): ........ × ........ = ........ cm²

Shape B (triangle): ½ ( ........ × ........ ) = ........ cm²

Total Area = ........ + ........ = ........ cm²

**d)** Draw a dotted line to divide this shape.

Shape A (rectangle): ........ × ........ = ........ cm²

Shape B (triangle): ½ ( ........ × ........ ) = ........ cm²

Total Area = ........ + ........ = ........ cm²

**Q8** Tariq is making a gravelled patio in the shape shown.
He can buy gravel in bags that cover 1 m² each.
How many bags of gravel does he need to buy?

........................................................................

# Areas

And now, finally, the sloping shapes — know the formulas and they're a piece of cake.

### Area of a Parallelogram = Base × Vertical Height

### Area of a Trapezium = ½ (a + b) × Height

**Q9** This parallelogram has an area of 4773 mm².
How long is its base?

43 mm

base

............................................................

**Q10** A metal blade for a craft knife is the shape of a <u>trapezium</u>.
Calculate the area of the metal.

70 mm

35 mm

155 mm

...........................................................................................................

...........................................................................................................

**Q11** A lawn is to be made 48 m².

**a)** If its width is 5 m, how long is it?

...........................................................................................................

**b)** Rolls of turf are 50 cm wide and 11 m long.
How many rolls need to be ordered to grass the lawn?

...........................................................................

Start by finding the area of 1 roll.
Then work out how many rolls
fit into the area of the lawn.

...........................................................................

# Circles

 Don't worry about that π bit — it just stands for the number 3.14159... Sometimes you'll be told to round it off to 3.14 or 3.142. If not, just use the π button on your calculator.

**Q1** On a separate piece of paper, draw a circle with radius 3 cm.
On your circle label the circumference, a radius and a diameter.

**Q2** A <u>minor sector</u> is labelled A on the diagram.
Name the features labelled:

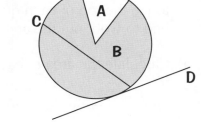

B: .................................

C: .................................   D: .................................

**Q3** Calculate the circumference of these circles.
Take π to be 3.14.

**a)**

2 cm   Circumference = π × diameter = ........................................

**b)** Circumference = π × diameter = ........................................

3.5 cm

**c)**

2.5 cm

Remember to work out the diameter first.

Diameter = radius × 2 = ........................................

Circumference = ........................................

**d)** A circle of radius 3.5 cm. ........................................................................

**Q4** A wheel has a diameter of 0.6 m. How far does it travel in one complete turn?
Give your answer to 2 d.p.

........................................................................

**Q5** What is the area of this semicircular rug?
Give your answer to the nearest whole number.

150 cm

Area = ........................................

# Circles

**Q6** Patrick is using weed killer to treat his circular lawn, which has a diameter of 12 m. The weed killer instructions say to use 20 ml for every square metre of lawn to be treated. How much weed killer does he need to use?  Give your answer to the nearest ml.

......................................................................................

**Q7** Anja made a cylindrical birthday cake of radius 15 cm.  She wanted to ice the top of each quarter in a different colour.  This meant she had to work out the area of each quarter of the cake to be iced.

**a)** Calculate the area of each quarter of the cake to be iced.

..............................................................................

**b)** Anja wanted to cut the cake in half and put a ribbon around one half.  How long would the ribbon have to be?

..............................................................................

**c)** Anja only had 50 cm of ribbon.  Would it be enough to put around a quarter of her cake?

..............................................................................

**Q8** This circular pond has a circular path around it.  The radius of the pond is 72 m and the path is 2 m wide.  Calculate to the nearest whole number:

**a)** the area of the pond.

..............................................................................

**b)** the area of paving stones needed to repave the path.

..............................................................................

**Q9** A bicycle wheel has a radius of 32 cm.  Calculate how far the bicycle will have travelled after the wheel has turned 100 times.  Give your answer to the nearest metre.

You only need to work out the distance covered by one of the wheels, as the bike will travel the same distance.

..............................................................................

..............................................................................

*SECTION FOUR — SHAPES AND AREA*

# Volume

Finding volumes of cubes and cuboids is just like finding areas of squares and rectangles — except you've got an extra side to multiply by.

**Q1**    A match box measures 7 cm by 4 cm by 5 cm.
What is its volume?

......................................................

**Q2**    What is the volume of a cube of side:

**a)** 5 cm? .............................................

**b)** 9 cm? .............................................

**c)** 15 cm? ............................................

**Q3**    Sam has a rectangular jelly mould measuring 16 cm by 16 cm by 6 cm.
Is the mould big enough to hold 1600 cm³ of jelly?

......................................................

**Q4**    A box measures 9 cm by 5 cm by 8 cm.

**a)** What is its volume? ...............................

**b)** What is the volume of a box twice
as long, twice as wide and twice as tall? ...........................................

**Q5**    Which holds more, a box measuring 12 cm by 5 cm by 8 cm or a box measuring
10 cm by 6 cm by 9 cm?

......................................................

**Q6**    A rectangular swimming pool is 12 m wide and 18 m long.
How many cubic metres of water are needed to fill the pool to a depth of 2 m?

......................................................

**Q7**    An ice cube measures 2 cm by 2 cm by 2 cm.  What is its volume? ........................
Is there enough room in a container measuring
8 cm by 12 cm by 10 cm for 100 ice cubes?     ......................................................

*SECTION FOUR — SHAPES AND AREA*

# Volume

**Q8**     Each shape has been made from centimetre cubes.  The volume of a centimetre cube is 1 cubic cm.  How many cubes are there in each shape?  What is the volume of each shape?

**a)**

There are  ..... cubes.
The volume is
        ..... cubic cm.

**b)**

There are  ..... cubes.
The volume is
        ..... cubic cm.

**c)**

There are  ..... cubes.
The volume is
        ..... cubic cm.

**d)**

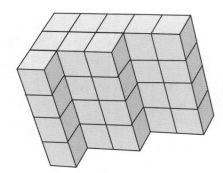

There are ..... cubes.
The volume is ..... cubic cm.

**e)**

There are ..... cubes.
The volume is ..... cubic cm.

**Q9**

Jill buys a bookshelf with the dimensions shown.

**a)** Find the cross-sectional area.

.............................................................................

**b)** Find the volume of the bookshelf in cm³.

.............................................................................

**Q10**     A right-angled triangular prism has the dimensions shown.
Find the volume of the prism in cm³.

.............................................................................

# Volume

Contrary to popular belief, there isn't anything that complicated about prisms — they're only solids with the same shape all the way through. The only bit that sometimes takes a bit longer is finding the cross-sectional area. (Back a few pages for a reminder of areas.)

**Volume of any prism =**
**Cross-sectional area**
**× Length**

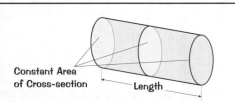

Constant Area
of Cross-section        Length

**Q11** A tree trunk can be thought of as a circular prism with a height of 1.7 m.
If the trunk has a diameter of 60 cm what volume of wood is this in m³?

..................................................................................................................

**Q12** A coffee mug is a cylinder closed at one end.
The internal radius is 7 cm and the internal height is 9 cm.

**a)** Taking π to be 3.14, find the volume of liquid the mug can hold.

..................................................................................................................

**b)** If 1200 cm³ of liquid is poured into the mug, find the depth to the nearest whole cm.

.......................................................................        The depth is just the length of
mug taken up by the liquid —
.......................................................................        which you find by rearranging
the volume formula.

**Q13** An unsharpened pencil can be thought of as a regular hexagonal prism with a
cylinder of graphite through the centre.

You need to use a
bit of Pythagoras
to find the height
of the triangles.

**a)** By considering a hexagon to be made up of six equilateral triangles,
calculate the area of the cross-section of the hexagonal prism shown.

...................................................................................

**b)** Find the area of wood in the cross-section.

circle
2mm
diameter

...................................................................................

hexagon 4mm each side

**c)** If the pencil is 20 cm long what is the volume of wood in the pencil?

...................................................................................

# Nets and Surface Area

**Q1** Which of the following nets would make a cube? .............................

a)

b)

c)

d)

e)

f)

**Q2** On a separate piece of paper, draw an accurate net for each of the following solids.

a)

5 cm

3 cm

4 cm

b)

3 cm

4 cm

2 cm

**Q3** A simple tent is to be made in the shape of a triangular prism.
The dimensions are shown in the diagram.

**a)** The two end-faces are isosceles triangles.
Find their areas.

.................................................

.................................................

3.4 m

3.2 m

2.3 m

4 m

**b)** The two sides are rectangles. Find their areas.

...................................................................................................................

**c)** The groundsheet is also a rectangle. Find its area.

...................................................................................................................

**d)** How much material is required to make this tent?

...................................................................................................................

**Q4** Hannah bought a bottle of perfume as a present in a cylindrical container, which was
20 cm tall and had a radius of 4 cm. She wanted to wrap the container in shiny red paper.
She has enough paper to cover an area of 600 cm$^2$. Is that enough to wrap the container?

...................................................................................................................

## Angles

Estimating angles is easy once you know the 4 special angles —
you can use them as reference points.

90°          180°          270°          360°

For each of the angles below write down its type, estimate its size (before you
measure it!) and finally measure each angle with a protractor.  The first one has
been done for you.

| Angle | Type | Estimated Size | Actual Size |
|---|---|---|---|
| a | acute | 40° | 43° |
| b | | | |
| c | | | |
| d | | | |
| e | | | |
| f | | | |

# Five Angle Rules

 Hope you've learnt those angle rules for a straight line and round a point...

**Q1** Work out the angles labelled:

a = .........

b = .........

c = .........

d = .........

e = .........

f = .........

g = .........

**The three angles inside a triangle always add up to 180°**

**Q2** Work out the missing angle in each of these triangles. The angles are not drawn to scale so you cannot measure them.

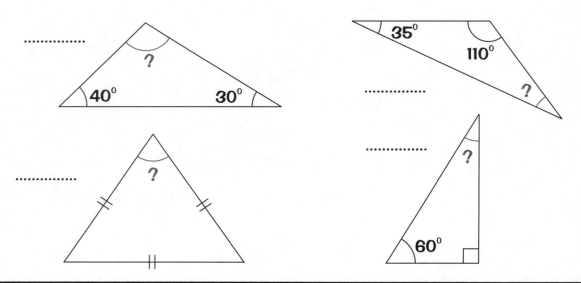

............... 40° 30° ?

35° 110° ? ...............

............... ?

............... ? 60°

*SECTION FIVE — ANGLES AND GEOMETRY*

# Five Angle Rules

| The angles in a quadrilateral always add up to 360° |

**Q3** Work out the missing angles in these quadrilaterals.

 **Three Letter Angle Notation** — bit of a mouthful, isn't it... but it's actually quite easy. Read and enjoy...

## Using Three Letters to Specify Angles

1) The <u>MIDDLE LETTER</u> tells you where the angle is.

2) The <u>OTHER TWO LETTERS</u> tell you which two lines enclose the angle.

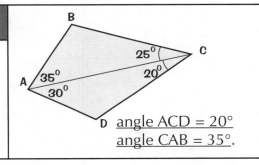

angle ACD = 20°
angle CAB = 35°.

**Q4 a)** State, with reasons, angle QRP.

..............................................................

**b)** Calculate angle RPQ.

..............................................................

**c)** What do all the angles sum to at P?

..............................................................

You'd better get learning these rules — they're not that hard, and you'll be well and truly stumped without them.

# Parallel and Perpendicular Lines

Once you know the **3 ANGLE RULES** for parallel lines, you can find all the angles out from just one — ah, such fun...

$c = f$ and $d = e$ — Alternate angles

$a = e$, $c = g$, $b = f$ and $d = h$ — Corresponding angles

$d + f = 180°$, $c + e = 180°$ — Supplementary angles

**Q1 a)** Lines A and B are parallel. Show this on the diagram.

**b)** Line C is perpendicular to A. Show this on the diagram.

**Q2** Find the sizes of the angles marked by letters in these diagrams.
Write down what sort of angle each one is.

**NOT DRAWN TO SCALE**

a = ...........................................

b = ...........................................

c = ...........................................

d = ...........................................

e = ...........................................

f = ...........................................

g = ...........................................

h = ...........................................

i = ...........................................

j = ...........................................

*SECTION FIVE — ANGLES AND GEOMETRY*

# Polygons and Angles

**These three handy formulas work for <u>all</u> polygons (regular or irregular):**

top tip

> **Sum of Exterior angles = 360°**
>
> **Interior angle = 180° – Exterior angle**
>
> **Sum of Interior angles = (n – 2) × 180°**

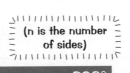
(n is the number of sides)

**This one works for <u>regular</u> polygons only:**  **Exterior angle = $\dfrac{360°}{n}$**

Interior angle
Exterior angle

**Q1**    A regular octagon has eight equal sides:

**a)** What is the size of one of its exterior angles? .......................

**b)** What is the size of one of its interior angles? .......................

Here is a regular pentagon:

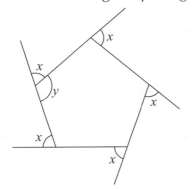

**c)** The five angles marked $x$ are its exterior angles. What do they add up to?

.........................................

**d)** Work out the value of $x$.

.........................................

**e)** Use your answer from part **d)** to work out the value of angle $y$.

.........................................

**Q2**    Charlotte is making a template for a patchwork quilt made from regular hexagons. She needs to measure and cut her template accurately before she uses it to cut the fabric.

**a)** How long should she make side $b$? ...............................

**b)** What is the size of angle $c$? ...............................

5 cm
$c$
$b$

**Q3**    Below is an irregular polygon. For any n-sided polygon, the sum of its interior angles is **(n – 2) × 180°**.

**a)** Find the sum of the interior angles.

...............................

**b)** Find the value of $x$.

...............................

# Transformations — Translation

Translations can be described using <u>vectors</u>.

The vector $\left(\begin{smallmatrix}2\\5\end{smallmatrix}\right)$ means move 2 spaces to the <u>right</u> and 5 spaces <u>up</u>.

The vector $\left(\begin{smallmatrix}-3\\-4\end{smallmatrix}\right)$ means move 3 spaces to the <u>left</u> and 4 spaces <u>down</u>.

**Q1** Translate the shapes A, B and C using these vectors: $A\left(\begin{smallmatrix}-4\\-3\end{smallmatrix}\right)$ $B\left(\begin{smallmatrix}5\\5\end{smallmatrix}\right)$ $C\left(\begin{smallmatrix}4\\-4\end{smallmatrix}\right)$
Label the images A′, B′ and C′.

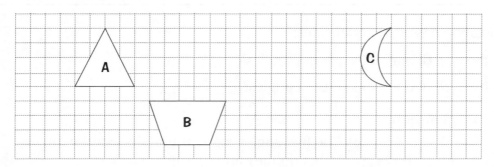

**Q2** Translate shape A below using the vectors given in order.
Draw the image each time, based on the last image you draw.

P $\left(\begin{smallmatrix}3\\4\end{smallmatrix}\right)$ Q $\left(\begin{smallmatrix}9\\2\end{smallmatrix}\right)$

R $\left(\begin{smallmatrix}3\\-4\end{smallmatrix}\right)$ S $\left(\begin{smallmatrix}-8\\-4\end{smallmatrix}\right)$

Label the images
A′, A″ , A‴, A⁗.

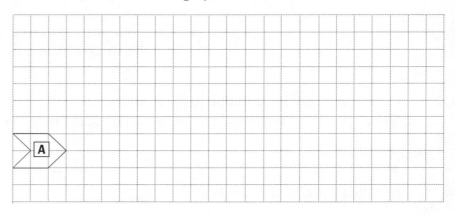

**Q3** Write down the <u>translation vectors</u> for the translations shown.

**a)** ................. **b)** ................. **c)** .................

*SECTION FIVE —ANGLES AND GEOMETRY*

# Transformations — Reflection

**Q1** Reflect each shape in the line $x = 4$.

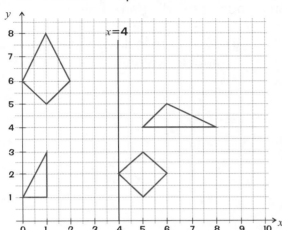

**Q2** Reflect the shapes in the line $y = x$.

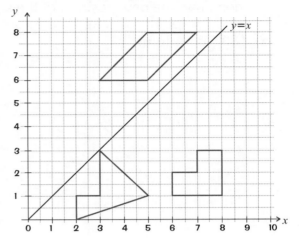

**Q3** Reflect ① in the line $y = 5$, label this ②.

Reflect ② in the line $x = 9$, label this ③.

Reflect ③ in the line $y = x$, label this ④.

Reflect ④ in the line $x = 4$, label this ⑤.

Reflect ⑤ in the line $y = x$, label this ⑥.

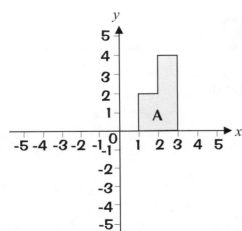

**Q4** **a)** Draw the result of reflecting shape A in the <u>x-axis</u>, label this A′.

**b)** Draw the result of reflecting shape A′ in the <u>y-axis</u>, label this A″.

**c)** What <u>single transformation</u> would turn shape A into shape A″?

..............................................................

**Nothing fancy here, is there? Reflection's just mirror drawing really. And we've all done that before...**

# Transformations — Rotation

**Q1** The centre of rotation for each of these diagrams is **X**. Rotate (turn) each shape as asked then draw the new position of the shape onto each of the diagrams below.

**a)** 180° (or ½ turn).

**b)** 270° anticlockwise (or ¾ turn anticlockwise).

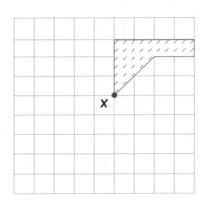

**Q2** This is a scalene triangle PQR. The centre of rotation is the origin 0.

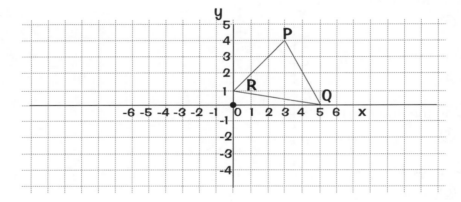

**a)** Write down the coordinates of...

P ............................ Q ............................ R ............................

**b)** Rotate the triangle 90° anticlockwise about the origin 0.
Label the new triangle P′ Q′ R′.

**c)** Write down the coordinates of ...

P′ ............................ Q′ ............................ R′ ............................

👉 A ½ turn clockwise is the same as a ½ turn anti-clockwise — and a ¼ turn clockwise is the same as a ¾ turn anti-clockwise. Great fun, innit...

*SECTION FIVE — ANGLES AND GEOMETRY*

# Transformations — Enlargement

The scale factor is a fancy way of saying HOW MUCH BIGGER the enlargement is than the original — e.g. a scale factor of 3 means it's <u>3 times as big</u>.

**Q1** Enlarge this triangle using scale factor 2 and centre of enlargement C.

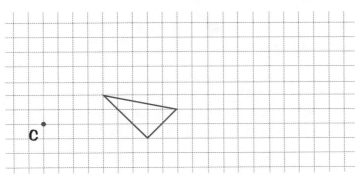

Remember,
scale factor = $\dfrac{\text{new length}}{\text{old length}}$

**Q2 a)** What is the scale factor of each of these enlargements?

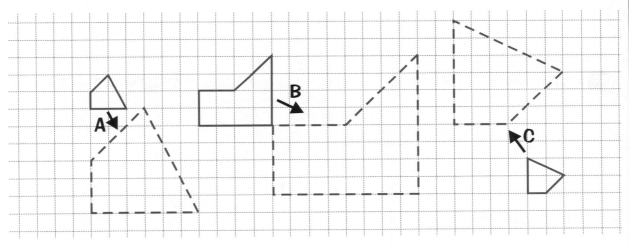

**A:** Scale factor is .............. **B:** Scale factor is .............. **C:** Scale factor is ..............

**b)** Mark the centre of enlargement for each of the shapes above.

**Q3** Enlarge this shape using scale factor 3 and centre of enlargement (-7, 1).

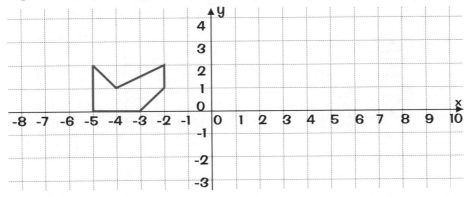

# Similar Shape Problems

**Q1** The side view of a playground swing is shown in the diagram. Triangle PST is an enlargement of triangle PQR.

Calculate the distance ST.

.........................................................

**Q2** Jenny has a photo on her computer which has a width of 640 pixels and a height of 480 pixels. She wants to enlarge the photo to use as her computer desktop background. The image must fill her monitor screen, which has a width of 1024 pixels.

**a)** Calculate the scale factor Jenny must use to enlarge her photo.

...........................................................................................................................

**b)** Work out the height of the enlarged photo, in pixels.

...........................................................................................................................

**Q3** Quadrilateral EFGH is an enlargement of quadrilateral ABCD with a scale factor of 3.

**a)** What is the value of x? .........................................

**b)** Calculate the length of side GH. .............................................................................

**Q4** The large rectangles in diagrams A and B (below) are similar. The small rectangles in the diagrams below are also similar. Find the shaded area of B.

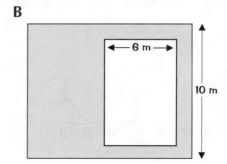

.........................................................

# Loci and Constructions

You've gotta be ultra neat with these — you'll lose easy marks if your pictures are scruffy — and let's face it, you'd rather have them, wouldn't you.

Constructions should always be done as accurately as possible using:

sharp pencil, ruler, compasses, protractor (set-square).

**Q1**  **a)** Draw a circle with radius 4 cm.

Draw in a diameter of the circle. Label one end of the diameter X and the other end Y.

Mark a point somewhere on the circumference — not too close to X or Y.  Label your point T. Join X to T and T to Y.

Measure angle XTY.

Angle XTY = .............°

**b)** Make an accurate drawing below of the triangle on the right. Measure side AB on your triangle, giving your answer in millimetres.

AB = ............. mm

# Loci and Constructions

Work through these questions bit by bit, and remember the following...

**LOCUS** — a line showing all points obeying the given rule.
**BISECTOR** — a line splitting an angle or line exactly in two.

**Q2 a)** In the space to the left, construct a triangle ABC with AB = 4 cm, BC = 5 cm, AC = 3 cm.

**b)** Construct the perpendicular bisector of AB and where this line meets BC, label the new point D.

**Q3**

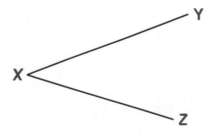

The diagram on the left shows two lines XY and XZ which meet at the point X. Construct the angle bisector of YXZ.

**Q4** On a plain piece of paper mark two points A and B which are 6 cm apart.

**a)** Draw the locus of points which are 4 cm from A.

**b)** Draw the locus of points which are 3 cm from B.

**c)** There are 2 points which are both 4 cm from A and 3 cm from B. Label them X and Y.

# Loci and Constructions

**Q5** A planner is trying to decide where to build a house. He is using the plan on the right, which shows the location of a canal, a TV mast (**A**) and a water main (**B**).

The house must be more than 100 m away from both the canal and the TV mast and be within 60 m of the water main.

Shade the area on the map where the planner could build the house.

**Q6** Tony likes to look at the tree in his garden. The diagram to the right shows the position of the tree relative to his bedroom window. Tony wants to position his bed in such a way that he can see the tree in the morning as he awakes.

Carefully <u>shade</u> on the diagram the area in which Tony could position his bed.

> He doesn't need to be able to see the whole tree.

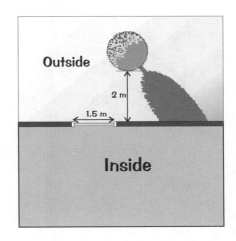

**Q7** With the aid of a pair of compasses accurately draw an equilateral triangle with sides 5 cm. Now accurately draw a square with sides 6 cm.

# Pythagoras' Theorem

**If you're as big a fan of Pythagoras as me, you'll ignore him and use this method instead:**

h(hypotenuse)

$a^2 + b^2 = h^2$

a

b

### The Simple Three Step Method

1) SQUARE the two numbers that you are given.
2) To find the <u>longest side, ADD</u> the two squared numbers.
   To find a <u>shorter side, SUBTRACT</u> the smaller one from the larger.
3) Take the SQUARE ROOT. Then check that your answer is sensible.

**Q1** Using Pythagoras' theorem, calculate the length of the third side in these triangles.

$c^2 = $ .......... + .......... = .........., $c = $ ..........

$d^2 = $ .......... − .......... = .........., $d = $ ..........

c

4 cm

3 cm

d

13 mm

5 mm

**Q2** Using Pythagoras' theorem, work out which of these triangles have right-angles.

10

A

8

6

12

B

8

4

3.5

6

C

4

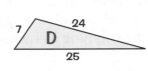

7

24

D

25

*If they don't have right-angles, the numbers won't fit the formula.*

...........................................................................................................................

...........................................................................................................................

**Q3** Calculate the missing lengths in these quadrilaterals. Give your answers to 3 sig. figs.

$e = $ ........................................................

$f = $ ........................................................

$g = $ ........................................................

$h = $ ........................................................

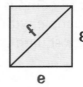

**Square**

f

8 mm

e

**Rhombus**

5 cm

g

8 cm

h

**Q4** A window cleaner needs to clean the upstairs windows of an office. He has a ladder 10 m long, but for safety reasons he can only put the bottom of it a minimum of 3 m away from the wall. In whole metres, what is the maximum height that the top of the ladder can reach when used safely?

.................................................................

.................................................................

.................................................................

10 m

3 m

# Metric and Imperial Units

These conversions will help you with the questions below. Handy, eh?

**APPROXIMATE CONVERSIONS**

| | | |
|---|---|---|
| 1 kg ≈ 2.2 lbs | 1 gallon ≈ 4.5 l | 1 foot ≈ 30 cm |
| 1 litre ≈ 1.75 pints | 1 mile ≈ 1.6 km (or 5 miles ≈ 8 km) | |

**Q1** The table shows the distances in miles between 4 cities in Scotland.
Fill in the blank table with the equivalent distances in kilometres.

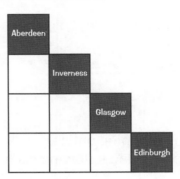

**Q2** Convert each of the following from kilograms to pounds.

10 kg = ..................... lbs          16 kg = ..................... lbs          75 kg = ..................... lbs

**Q3** David is throwing a party for himself and 15 of his friends.
He decides that it would be nice to make a bowl
of fruit punch and carefully follows a recipe
to make 8 pints.

**a)** Will David fit all the punch in his 5 litre bowl?

.......................................................................

**b)** Is there enough punch for everyone at the party to have
one 300 ml glass?

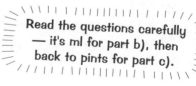

Read the questions carefully
— it's ml for part b), then
back to pints for part c).

.......................................................................................

**c)** In the end, 12 people split the punch equally between them.
How many pints did they each drink?

.......................................................................................

**Q4** The average fuel efficiency of two cars is shown below. Which car is the most efficient?
Car A — 53 miles per gallon
Car B — 4.5 litres per 100 km

Hint: 4.5 litres = 1 gallon

.......................................................................................

# Converting Units

The method for these questions is very easy so you might as well learn it...

> 1) Find the <u>Conversion Factor</u>
>
> 2) <u>Multiply by it AND divide by it</u>
>
> 3) Choose the <u>common sense answer</u>

The conversion factor is the link between the two units — e.g. there are 100 cm in a m so the conversion factor is 100.

**Q1** Fill in the gaps using the conversion factors:

20 mm = ............... cm              ............... mm = 6 cm              3470 m = ............... km

............... m = 2 km              3 km = ............... cm              ............... mm = 3.4 m

8550 g = ............... kg              1.2 l = ............... ml              4400 ml = ............... l

**Q2** Justin is shopping online.
He looks up the following exchange rates:

> 1.60 US Dollars ($) to £1 Sterling.
> 150 Japanese Yen (¥) to £1 Sterling.
> 2 Australian Dollars (AUD) to £1 Sterling.

Use these exchange rates to calculate to the nearest penny the cost in Sterling of each of Justin's purchases:

**a)** A book costing $7.50

.................................................

**b)** An MP3 player costing ¥7660

.................................................

**c)** An electric guitar costing 683 AUD

.................................................

**d)** Justin has two quotes for the cost of shipping his guitar from Australia to the UK:
155 AUD from an Australian courier and £76.45 from a British courier.
Which company is cheaper?

.................................................

**Q3** Jeremy is driving at 65 mph. The speed limit is 100 km/h.
How many km/h over the speed limit is Jeremy driving?

.................................................

**Q4** Chris wants to varnish the surface of his table, which has an area of 1200 cm$^2$.
He buys a tin of varnish that says it will cover an area of 2 m$^2$.

Find the area of the table surface in m$^2$.
Does Chis have enough varnish to cover the surface of his table?

.................................................

# Rounding and Estimating Measurements

**Q1**

The spade is almost 1 m tall.
Estimate the height of the sunflower
in metres.

..................................

\\\ \\ | | | /// | | | | | | | | | | | | | | | ///
If you have trouble estimating the height by
eye, try measuring the spade against your
finger. Then see how many times that bit of
finger fits into the height of the sunflower.
/ / | | | | | | | | | | | | | | | \ \ \

**Q2**   The number of drawing pins in the box has been rounded to the nearest 10.

What is the least possible number
of drawing pins in the box?

..............

**Q3**   A rectangular rug is 2 metres long and 1 metre wide.
Both measurements are given correct to the nearest metre.

**a)** State the minimum possible length of the rug.

..................................................................................................................

**b)** Calculate the maximum possible width of the rug.

..................................................................................................................

**Q4**   Matt is buying skirting board to fit to a wall which measures 540 cm to 2 s.f.
What length of board should Matt buy to guarantee he has enough for the
whole wall?

.................................................

When you round numbers off to the nearest unit, the **ACTUAL**
number could be up to **HALF A UNIT** bigger or smaller...

# Reading Scales and Timetables

**Q1** **a)** What is the weight of these two apples?

.............................

**b)** How much juice is in this jug?

.............................

**Q2** The times below are given using the 24 hour system. Using am or pm, give the equivalent time for a 12 hour clock.

**a)** 0400 ........................

**b)** 0215 ........................

**c)** 2130 ........................

**Q3** The times below are taken from a 12 hour clock. Give the equivalent 24 hour readings.

**a)** 11.22 am .......................

**b)** 12.30 pm .......................

**c)** 3.33 pm .......................

**Q4** Convert the following into hours and minutes:

**a)** 3.75 hours .......................

**b)** 0.2 hours .......................

**c)** 5.8 hours .......................

**Q5** Fran is going to cook a 5.5 kg ham. The ham needs to be cooked for 40 minutes per kg, and then left to "rest" for 25 minutes before serving. Fran wants to serve the ham at 4 pm, what time should she start cooking?

.................................................................................................

**Q6** Steve sets off on a bike ride at 10.30 am. He stops for lunch at 12.15 pm and sets off again at 1 pm. He has a 20 minute rest stop in the afternoon and gets home at 4.50 pm.

How long did he cycle for altogether? ...............................................................

**Q7** This timetable refers to three trains that travel from Asham to Derton.

**a)** Which train is quickest from Asham to Derton? ...............................................................

**b)** Which train is quickest from Cottingham to Derton?

...............................................

**c)** I live in Bordhouse. It takes me 8 minutes to walk to the train station. At what time must I leave the house by to arrive in Derton before 2.30 pm?

| Asham – Derton | | | |
|---|---|---|---|
| | Train 1 | Train 2 | Train 3 |
| **Asham** | 0832 | 1135 | 1336 |
| **Bordhouse** | 0914 | 1216 | 1414 |
| **Cottingham** | 1002 | 1259 | 1456 |
| **Derton** | 1101 | 1404 | 1602 |

.................................................................................................

*SECTION SIX — MEASURES*

# Compass Directions and Bearings

**Q1**

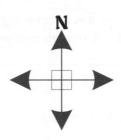

Start at the dot in the middle of the bottom line and follow the directions.

**a)** West 4 squares.
**b)** North 4 squares.
**c)** East 4 squares.
**d)** South 4 squares.
**e)** North East through 2 squares.

**f)** North 4 squares.
**g)** South West through 2 squares.
**h)** West 4 squares.
**i)** North East through 2 squares.
**j)** East 4 squares.

What shape have you drawn? ......................

**Q2**

**Joe's house**

**Shop**

**Church**

**Sue's house**

**Park**

**Jane's house**

**a)** What direction does Jane go to get to Sue's house? ...................................

**b)** What direction is the church from Joe's house? ...................................

**c)** What is South East of Sue's house? ...................................

**d)** What is West of Sue's house? ...................................

**e)** Jane is at home. She is going to meet Sue in the park. They are going to the shop and then to Joe's house. Write down Jane's directions.

...................................................................................................................................

*SECTION SIX — MEASURES*

# Compass Directions and Bearings

Bearings always have three digits — even the small ones...
in other words, if you've measured 60°, you've got to write it as 060°.

This is a map of part of a coastline.  The scale is one cm to one km.

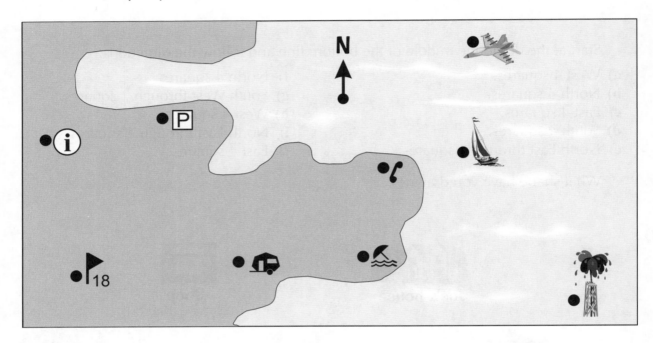

**Q3**    What is the bearing of the 🚐 from the ⓘ? ....................................................

**Q4**    What is the bearing of the P from the 🏊? ....................................................

**Q5**    How far and on what bearing is:

**a)** The boat from the plane? .........................................................

**b)** The boat from the oil rig? .........................................................

**c)** The plane from the oil rig? .........................................................

**Q6**    The water ski centre is on a bearing of 050° from the golf course, ▶₁₈, and at a distance of 4.5 km.  Put a ☆ where the water ski centre is.

> Do the direction bit first — and draw a straight line.  Then measure the correct distance along it.

**Q7**    There is a lighthouse on the coast.  It is at a bearing of 300° from the oil rig and a bearing of 270° from the boat.  Mark its position with a △.

# Maps and Scale Drawings

**Q1** The scale on this map is 1 cm : 4 km.

a) Measure the distance from A to B in cm. ...................................

b) What is the actual distance from A to B in km? ...................................

c) A helicopter flies on a direct route from A to B, B to C and C to D.
What is the total distance flown in km?

...................................................................

d) Angus walks 8 km from point B on a bearing of 130°.
Mark his new position on the map and label it E.

**Q2** Frank has made a scale drawing of his garden to help him plan some improvements.
The scale on the drawing is 1 : 50.

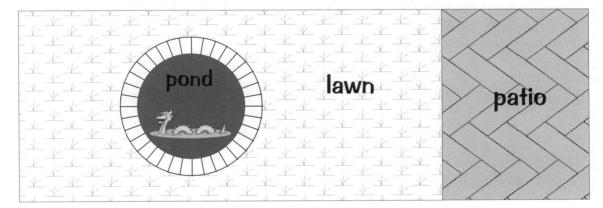

a) Frank wants to put up a fence along the three outside edges of the lawn.
How many metres of fencing does he need to buy?

...................................

b) What are the actual dimensions of Frank's patio in m?

...................................

If the scale doesn't say what units it's in, it just means that both sides of
the ratio are the same units — so <u>1 : 1000</u> would mean <u>1 cm : 1000 cm</u>.

# Maps and Scale Drawings

Watch out for those units... there's quite a mixture here —
you'll have to convert some of them before you can go anywhere.

**Q3**   A rectangular room measures 20 m long and 15 m wide.  Work out the measurements
for a scale drawing of the room using a scale of 1 cm = 2 m.

Length = .......................................   Width = .......................................

**Q4**   Katie drew a scale drawing of the top of her
desk.  She used a scale of 1:10. This is her
drawing of the computer keyboard.  What are
the actual dimensions of it?

Length = .......................................   Width = .......................................

**Q5**   | Cupboards | Oven | Cupboards |

This is a scale drawing of part of Paul's kitchen.
Measure the width of the gap for the oven.

.................. mm.

The drawing uses a scale of 1 : 60.
Work out the maximum width of oven, in cm, that Paul can buy.

.............................................................................................................

**Q6**   A rectangular field is 60 m long and 40 m wide.  The farmer needs to make a scale
drawing of it.  He uses a scale of 1 : 2000.  Work out the measurements for the scale
drawing.  (Hint — change the m to cm.)

.............................................................................................................

.............................................................................................................

**Q7**   A rectangular room is 4.8 m long and 3.6 m wide.  Make a scale drawing of it using
a scale of 1 cm to 120 cm.  First work out the measurements for the scale drawing.

Length = ...................................

Width = ...................................

On your scale drawing mark a window, whose actual
length is 2.4 m, on one long wall and mark a door,
actual width 90 cm, on one short wall.

Window = ...................................

Door = ...................................

# Speed

This is an easy enough formula — and of course you can put it in that good old formula triangle as well.

$$\text{Average speed} = \frac{\text{Total distance}}{\text{Total time}}$$

**Q1**  A motorbike travels for 3 hours at an average speed of 55 mph.  How far has it travelled?

.........................................................................................................................................

**Q2**  <u>Complete</u> this table

| Distance Travelled | Time taken | Average Speed |
|---|---|---|
| 210 km | 3 hrs | |
| 135 miles | | 30 mph |
| | 2 hrs 30 mins | 42 km/h |
| 9 miles | 45 mins | |
| 640 km | | 800 km/h |
| | 1 hr 10 mins | 60 mph |

**Q3**  An athlete can run 100 m in 11 seconds.
Calculate the athlete's speed in:

**a)** m/s

.................................................................

**b)** km/h

.................................................................

**Q4**  Simon is driving on the motorway at an average speed of 67 mph.
He sees a sign telling him that he is 36 miles away from the next service station.

**a)** To the nearest minute, how long will it take Simon to reach the service station?

.........................................................................................................................................

**b)** Later, Simon drove through some roadworks where the speed limit was 50 mph.
Two cameras recorded the time taken to travel 1200 m through the roadworks as
56 seconds.  Was Simon speeding through the roadworks?

....................................................................

**Remember —**
**1 mile ≈ 1.6 km**

*SECTION SIX — MEASURES*

# Density

Here we go again — the multi-purpose formula triangle.  Learn the positions of M, D and V, plug in the numbers and pull out the answer... magic.

$$\text{DENSITY} = \frac{\text{mass}}{\text{volume}}$$

**Q1**    Find the <u>density</u> of each of these pieces of wood, giving your answer in g/cm³:

a) Mass 3 g, volume 4 cm³

..................................

b) Mass 20 g, volume 25 cm³

..................................

c) Mass 12 kg, volume 20 000 cm³

..................................

d) Mass 14 kg, volume 0.02 m³.

..................................

**Q2**    Calculate the <u>mass</u> of each of these objects:

a) a small marble statue of density
2.6 g/cm³ and volume 24 cm³         ..................................

b) a plastic cube of volume 64 cm³
and density 1.5 g/cm³               ..................................

c) a gold ingot with density 19.5 g/cm³
measuring 12 cm by 4 cm by 4 cm     ..................................

d) a pebble with volume 30 cm³
and density 2.5 g/cm³.              ..................................

**Q3**    Work out the <u>volume</u> of each of these items:

a) a bag of sugar of mass 1 kg and density 1.6 g/cm³

..................................

b) a packet of margarine with density 2.8 g/cm³ and mass 250 g

..................................

c) a 50 kg sack of coal with density 1.8 g/cm³

..................................

d) a box of cereal with density 0.2 g/cm³ and mass 500 g.

..................................

## Collecting Data

**Q1**    Cheapeez supermarket wants to find out what they should stock to attract more customers.  They interview the first 100 people to go into their store one Saturday morning.

    **a)** Give one reason why this sample will produce biased data.

    ......................................................................................................................................

    **b)** What population should have been sampled from?

    ......................................................................................................................................

**Q2**    Fred is trying to find out why people use public transport.
He surveys a sample of 100 people passing through the town bus station between 5.30 pm and 6.30 pm on a Monday evening.

    **a)** Give one reason why Fred's sample is biased.

    ......................................................................................................................................

    **b)** Say how Fred could improve his sample to avoid bias.

    ......................................................................................................................................

**Q3**    Sally wants to do a survey to find out how the students in her class travel to school.
Design a data-collection sheet she could use to collect her data.

**Q4**    Peter wants to find out whether the students at his school like maths.
In his survey, he asks the question: "Do you agree maths is the worst subject?"
State one problem with this question.

    ......................................................................................................................................

# Collecting Data

Questionnaires are a great way to gather information. But you need to think carefully about how you design, distribute and collect them so you get the information you want.

**Q5**  Stanley is researching the use of the school canteen.
He asks this question to a sample of students at the school:
*How often do you use the canteen? Tick one of the boxes.*

*Very often*  ☐     *Quite often*  ☐     *Not very often*  ☐

**a)** Give one criticism of Stanley's question.

.............................................................................................................

**b)** Write a question that Stanley could use to find out how often students at his school use the canteen.

.............................................................................................................

**Q6**  A cafe owner is trying to find out which drinks his customers prefer.
He asks them to complete a questionnaire including this question:
*What is your favourite drink?*

     i)  **Tea**       ii)  **Coffee**
    iii)  **Fruit squash**       iv)  **Other**

52 of the first 100 people to answer reply "other".

**a)** Give one criticism of the question.

.............................................................................................................

**b)** How could the question be improved?

.............................................................................................................

**Q7**  Peter compiles a questionnaire on music tastes and sends it to a sample of 100 students at his school. He only receives 55 questionnaires back.

**a)** State one problem that Peter could have with his data.

.............................................................................................................

**b)** What could Peter do to avoid this problem?

.............................................................................................................

*SECTION SEVEN — STATISTICS AND PROBABILITY*

# Mean, Median, Mode and Range

*To find the <u>mode</u>, put the data in order of size first — then it's easier to see which number you've got most of.*

**Q1** Find the mode for each of these sets of data.

**a)** 3,   5,   8,   6,   3,   7,   3,   5,   3,   9

................................................................ Mode is ..........

**b)** 52,   26,   13,   52,   31,   12,   26,   13,   52,   87,   41

................................................................ Mode is ..........

**Q2** The temperature in °C on 10 summer days in England was:

25,   18,   23,   19,   23,   24,   23,   18,   20,   19

What was the modal temperature?

................................................................ Modal temperature is ..........°C.

**Q3** The time it takes thirty pupils in a class to get to school each day in minutes is:

18,   24,   12,   28,   17,   34,   17,   17,   28,   12,   23,   24,   17,   34,   9,
32,   15,   31,   17,   19,   17,   32,   15,   17,   21,   29,   34,   17,   12,   17

What is the modal time?

.................................................................................................

.................................................................................................

Modal time is ............ mins.

*Put the data in order of size for <u>median</u> questions too — it's much easier to find the middle value.*

**Q4** Find the median for these sets of data.

**a)** 3,   6,   7,   12,   2,   5,   4,   2,   9

.................................................................... Median is ............

**b)** 14,   5,   21,   7,   19,   3,   12,   2,   5

.................................................................... Median is ............

**Q5** These are the heights of fifteen 16 year olds.

162 cm      156 cm      174 cm      148 cm      152 cm      139 cm      167 cm      134 cm
157 cm      163 cm      149 cm      134 cm      158 cm      172 cm      146 cm

What is the median height?  Write your answer in the shaded box.

| | | | | | | | | | | | | | | Median |
|---|---|---|---|---|---|---|---|---|---|---|---|---|---|---|

# Mean, Median, Mode and Range

Yikes — MEAN questions... well, they're not as bad as everyone makes out.
Remember to include zeros in your calculations — they still count.

**Q6** Find the mean of each of the sets of data below. If necessary, round your answers to 1 decimal place:

*Remember the formula for mean — total of the items ÷ number of items.*

**a)** 13, 15, 11, 12, 16, 13, 11, 9 = ............

**b)** 16, 13, 2, 15, 0, 9 = ............

**c)** 80, 70, 80, 50, 60, 70, 90, 60, 50, 70, 70 = ............

**Q7** Now find the mean for each of these sets of data:

**a)** 5, 3, 7, 3, 2 = .............................................................................................

**b)** 7, 3, 9, 5, 3, 5, 4, 6, 2, 6 = .........................................................................

**Q8** The number of goals scored by a hockey team over a period of 10 games is listed below.

0, 3, 2, 4, 1, 2, 3, 4, 1, 0.

What is the range of the number of goals scored? ............................................

**Q9** Sarah and her friends were measured and their heights were found to be:

1.52 m, 1.61 m, 1.49 m, 1.55 m, 1.39 m, 1.56 m.

What is the range of the heights? ............................................

**Q10** Here are the times 6 people took to do a Maths test:

1 hour 10 mins, 2 hours 10 mins, 1 hour 35 mins,
1 hours 55 min, 1 hour 18 mins, 2 hours 15 mins.

What is the range of these times? ..................................................................

**Q11** David is on a diet. He needs to have a mean calorie intake of 1900 calories a day. The table below shows how many calories he has eaten so far this week.

How many calories must David eat on Friday to make sure that his mean intake for the five days is correct?

............................................

| Day | Calories Eaten |
|-----------|----------------|
| Monday | 1875 |
| Tuesday | 2105 |
| Wednesday | 1680 |
| Thursday | 1910 |
| Friday | |

# Tables, Charts and Pictograms

**Make sure you read these questions carefully. You don't want to lose easy marks by looking at the wrong bit of the table or chart.**

**Q1** The local library is carrying out a survey to find the amount of time people spend reading each day. Complete the frequency table below, then draw a frequency polygon to show the results.

| Time spent reading (mins) | Tally | Frequency |
|---|---|---|
| 1 - 15 | HHT I | 6 |
| 16 - 30 | HHT III | |
| 31 - 45 | III | |
| 46 - 60 | HHT | |
| 61 - 75 | III | |

FREQUENCY

TIME SPENT READING (MIN)

**Q2** One hundred vehicles on a road were recorded as part of a traffic study. Use this two-way table to answer the following questions.

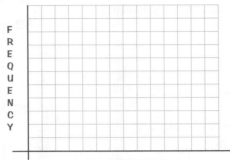

| | Van | Motor-bike | Car | Total |
|---|---|---|---|---|
| Travelling North | 15 | | | 48 |
| Travelling South | 20 | | 23 | |
| Total | | 21 | | 100 |

**a)** How many vans were recorded? ..........

**b)** How many vehicles in the survey were travelling south? ..........

**c)** How many motorbikes were travelling south? ..........

**d)** How many cars were travelling north? ..........

**Q3** This pictogram shows the favourite drinks of a group of pupils.

| Favourite Drinks | Number of Pupils |
|---|---|
| Lemonade | ✦ ✦ ✦ ✦ ✦ ✦ ✦ ✦ ✦ |
| Cola | ✦ ✦ ✦ ✦ ✦ ✦ ✦ ✦ ✦ ✦ |
| Cherryade | ✦ ✦ ✦ ✦ ✦ ✦ |
| Orange Squash | ✦ ✦ ✦ |
| Milk | ✦ |

✦ Represents 2 pupils.

**a)** How many pupils were questioned? ........................................ pupils.

**b)** How many pupils prefer non-fizzy drinks? ........................................ pupils.

**c)** 18 pupils liked lemonade best. How many more liked cola best? .................. pupils.

**d)** Comment on the popularity of cola compared with milk.

..................................................................................................................

*SECTION SEVEN — STATISTICS AND PROBABILITY*

# Line Graphs

Drawing line graphs is easy — just plot the points,
then join them up with straight lines.

**Q1** Billy took his temperature and recorded it on this graph.

What was his temperature at:

**a)** 10 am? .....................

**b)** 2 pm? .....................

**c)** What was his highest
temperature?

..................

**d)** When was this? .....................

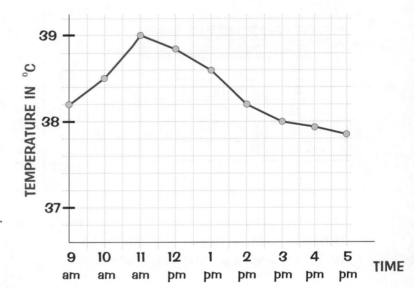

**Q2** David weighed himself every 5 days. The results are given below.
Draw a graph to show how David's weight changed.

| DAY N° | 0 | 5 | 10 | 15 | 20 | 25 | 30 |
|--------|------|------|------|------|------|------|------|
| WEIGHT KG | 88.9 | 88.4 | 87.6 | 87.5 | 87.5 | 87.2 | 87.0 |

In your own words, describe how
David's weight changed:

.................................................

.................................................

.................................................

.................................................

# Bar Charts

**Q1**    Here is a bar chart showing pupils' favourite colours:

a) How many like blue best?  ..............

b) How many more people
chose red than yellow?  ..............

c) How many pupils took part in the survey?  ..............

d) What fraction of the class prefer green?  ..............

**Favourite Colour**

**Q2**    The bar chart on the left shows the marks from a test done by some students.

a) How many students
scored 20 marks or less?  ..............

b) The pass mark for this test was 31.
How many students passed the test?  ..............

c) How many students took the test?  ..............

**Q3**    Megan records whether people choose pizza or pasta in her Italian restaurant. The dual bar chart shows the results over one week.

a) On which days was pizza more popular?

......................................................

b) On which day did Megan
have the most customers?  ....................

**Q4**    The graphs below show the marital status of men and women aged 65 and over.

a) What proportion of males
aged 65-69 are married?

......................................

b) What proportion of
females aged 75-79 are
divorced or separated?

......................................

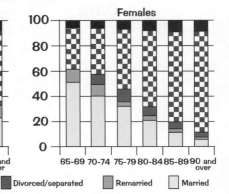

# Pie Charts

**Q1** This table shows the daily amount of air time of programme types on TV:

| Programme | Hours | Angle |
|---|---|---|
| News | 5 | 75 |
| Sport | 3 | |
| Music | 2 | |
| Current Affairs | 3 | |
| Comedy | 2 | |
| Other | 9 | |
| Total | 24 | |

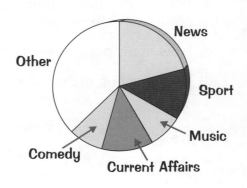

Using an angle measurer, complete the table by finding
the size of the angle represented by each type of programme.
The first angle is done for you.

**Q2** Sandra is giving a presentation on her company's budget. She has decided to present
the budget as a pie chart. The company spends £54 000 each week on various items,
which are shown on the pie chart below.

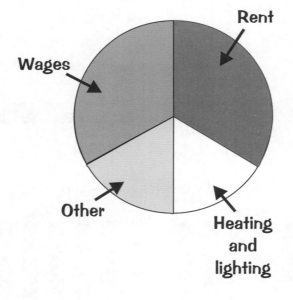

a) What fraction of the budget is
spent on wages each week?

......................................................

b) How much money is spent on
wages each week?

......................................................

c) What fraction of the budget is spent
on heating and lighting each week?

......................................................

d) How much money is spent on
heating and lighting each week?

......................................................

# Pie Charts

**Q3** In a University department there are 180 students from different countries.

| Country | UK | Malaysia | Spain | Others |
|---|---|---|---|---|
| Number of students | 90 | 35 | 10 | 45 |

To show this on a pie chart you have to work out the angle of each sector.
Complete the table showing your working. The UK is done for you.

| COUNTRY | WORKING | ANGLE in degrees |
|---|---|---|
| UK | 90 ÷ 180 × 360 = | 180° |
| MALAYSIA | | |
| SPAIN | | |
| OTHERS | | |

Now complete the pie chart using an angle measurer. The UK sector is done for you.

**Q4** Pupils at a school were asked about their activities at weekends. The results are shown in the table. Complete the table and then draw the pie chart using an angle measurer.

| ACTIVITY | HOURS | WORKING | ANGLE |
|---|---|---|---|
| Homework | 6 | 6 ÷ 48 × 360 = | 45° |
| Sport | 2 | | |
| TV | 10 | | |
| Computer games | 2 | | |
| Sleeping | 18 | | |
| Listening to music | 2 | | |
| Paid work | 8 | | |
| Total | 48 | | |

**Q5** The pie charts opposite appear in a newspaper article about a local election. Nicki says that more people voted for the Green party in 2009 than in 2005.

Comment on <u>whether it's possible</u> to tell this from the pie charts.

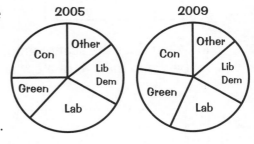

....................................................................................

....................................................................................

> The full circle (that's all 360° of it) represents the total of everything —
> so you shouldn't find any gaps in it, basically.

# Scatter Graphs

**Q1** The scatter graphs below show the relationship between:

**a)** The temperature of the day and the amount of ice cream sold.

**b)** The price of ice cream and the amount sold.

**c)** The age of customers and the amount of ice cream sold.

**a)**

**b)**

**c)**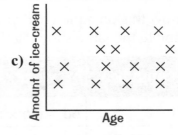

Describe the correlation of each graph and say what each graph tells you.

**a)** ............................................................................................................................

**b)** ............................................................................................................................

**c)** ............................................................................................................................

**Q2** Alice wanted to buy a second hand car. She wrote down the ages and prices of 15 similarly-sized cars on sale locally. Draw a scatter graph for Alice's information.

| Age of car (years) | Price (£) |
|---|---|
| 4 | 4995 |
| 2 | 7995 |
| 3 | 6595 |
| 1 | 7995 |
| 5 | 3495 |
| 8 | 4595 |
| 9 | 1995 |
| 1 | 7695 |
| 2 | 7795 |
| 6 | 3995 |
| 5 | 3995 |
| 1 | 9195 |
| 3 | 5995 |
| 4 | 4195 |
| 9 | 2195 |

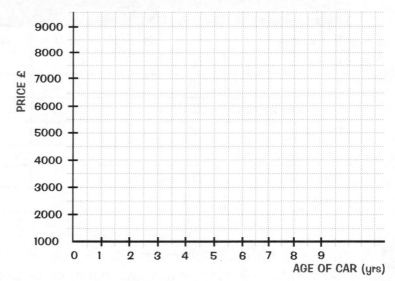

**a)** What does the scatter graph tell you about the relationship between the age of a car and its price?

..............................................................................................................................

**b)** By drawing a line of best fit, predict the price of an 8-year-old car. .................

The big word examiners like using in these questions is **CORRELATION** — and they're very keen on it, so make sure you know what it means.

*SECTION SEVEN — STATISTICS AND PROBABILITY*

# Stem and Leaf Diagrams

**Q1**    This stem and leaf diagram shows the ages of people in a cinema.

```
1 |  2 2 4 8 8 9 9
2 |  0 1 1 2 5 6
3 |  0 0 0 5
4 |  2 5 9
5 |
6 |  8
```

**Key: 2 | 5 means 25**

**a)** How many people in the cinema were in their twenties?    .................

**b)** Write out the ages of all of the people in the cinema below.

................................................................................

**Q2**    This stem and leaf diagram shows the exam scores of a group of Year 9 pupils.

**a)** How many pupils got a score between 60 and 70? ........................

**b)** How many scored 80 or more? ........................

**c)** What was the most common test score? ........................

**d)** How many scored less than 50? ........................

**e)** How many pupils took the test? ........................

```
3 |  2 3
4 |  6 8 8
5 |  1 2 2 3 6 6 9
6 |  1 5 5 5 8
7 |  2 3 4 5 8
8 |  0 1 1 5
9 |  0 2 3
```

**Key: 5 | 2 means 52**

**Q3**    I've been measuring the length of beetles for a science project.  Here are the lengths in millimetres:

    12  18  20  11  31
    19  27  34  19  22

**a)** Complete the stem and leaf diagram on the right to show the results above.

```
1 |
2 |
3 |
```

**Key: 2 | 2 means 22**

**b)** From your stem and leaf diagram, find the range of the data.

................................................................................

**c)** Find the median of the data.

................................................................................

Stem and leaf diagrams are easy once you understand how they work.
Just remember that the digit to the left of the line is the 'tens' digit.

# Frequency Tables and Averages

**Q1**  Last season Newcaster City played 32 matches.
The number of goals they scored in each match were recorded as shown.

| 2 | 4 | 3 | 5 |
|---|---|---|---|
| 1 | 0 | 3 | 2 |
| 4 | 2 | 1 | 2 |
| 0 | 2 | 3 | 1 |
| 1 | 0 | 0 | 1 |
| 1 | 1 | 1 | 0 |
| 1 | 3 | 2 | 0 |
| 1 | 1 | 0 | 4 |

| GOALS | TALLY | FREQUENCY |
|-------|-------|-----------|
| 0     |       |           |
| 1     |       |           |
| 2     |       |           |
| 3     |       |           |
| 4     |       |           |
| 5     |       |           |

a) Complete the tally chart of the goals.

b) What was the modal number of goals scored in each match?

........................................................................................................................

c) What was the median number of goals scored in each match?

........................................................................................................................

d) What was the range of goals scored over the whole season?

........................................................................................................................

**Q2**  The frequency table below shows the number of hours spent
Christmas shopping by 100 people surveyed in a town centre.

| Number of Hours | 0 | 1 | 2 | 3 | 4 | 5 | 6 | 7 | 8 |
|-----------------|---|---|---|---|---|---|---|---|---|
| Frequency | 1 | 9 | 10 | 10 | 11 | 27 | 9 | 15 | 8 |
| Hours × Frequency | | | | | | | | | |

a) What is the modal number of hours spent Christmas shopping? ............

b) Fill in the third row of the table.

c) What is the total amount of time spent Christmas shopping by all the people surveyed?

........................................................................................................................

d) What is the mean amount of time spent Christmas shopping by a person?

........................................................................................................................

# Grouped Frequency Tables

As a rule these are trickier than standard frequency tables — you'll certainly have to tread carefully here. Have a good look at the box below and make sure you remember it.

## Mean and Mid-Interval Values

1) The **MID-INTERVAL VALUES** are just what they sound like — the middle of the group.
2) Using the Frequencies and Mid-Interval Values you can estimate the **MEAN**.

$$\text{Estimated Mean} = \frac{\text{Overall Total (Frequency} \times \text{Mid-interval value)}}{\text{Frequency total}}$$

| Shoe Size | 1 - 2 | 3 - 4 | 5 - 6 | 7 - 8 | Totals |
|---|---|---|---|---|---|
| Frequency | 15 | 10 | 3 | 1 | 29 |
| Mid-Interval Value | 1.5 | 3.5 | 5.5 | 7.5 | — |
| Frequency x Mid-Interval Value | 22.5 | 35 | 16.5 | 7.5 | 81.5 |

So the estimated mean value is 81.5 ÷ 29 = 2.81

---

**Q1** In a survey of test results in a French class at Blugdon High, these grades were achieved by the 23 pupils:

a) Write down the mid-interval values for each of the groups.

| (grade) score | (E) 31-40 | (D) 41-50 | (C) 51-60 | (B) 61-70 |
|---|---|---|---|---|
| frequency | 4 | 7 | 8 | 4 |

.................................................................................................................

b) Calculate an estimate for the mean value.

.................................................................................................................

.................................................................................................................

**Q2** Dean is carrying out a survey for his Geography coursework. He asked 80 people how many miles they drove their car last year to the nearest thousand. He has started filling in a grouped frequency table to show his results.

| No. of Miles (thousands) | 1 - 10 | 11 - 20 | 21 - 30 | 31 - 40 | 41 - 50 | 51 - 60 | 61 - 70 | 71 - 80 | 81 - 90 | 91 - 100 |
|---|---|---|---|---|---|---|---|---|---|---|
| No. of Cars | 2 | 3 | 5 | 19 | 16 | 14 | 10 | 7 | | |

a) Complete Dean's table using the following information:
   81 245,  82 675,  90 159,  90 569

b) Write down the modal class. ....................................

c) Which class contains the median number of miles driven? ....................................

# Grouped Frequency Tables

**Q3** This table shows times for each team of swimmers, the Dolphins and the Sharks.

| Dolphins | | | Sharks | | |
|---|---|---|---|---|---|
| Time interval (seconds) | Frequency | Mid-interval value | Time interval (seconds) | Frequency | Mid-interval value |
| $14 \leq t < 20$ | 3 | 17 | $14 \leq t < 20$ | 6 | 17 |
| $20 \leq t < 26$ | 7 | 23 | $20 \leq t < 26$ | 15 | 23 |
| $26 \leq t < 32$ | 15 | | $26 \leq t < 32$ | 33 | |
| $32 \leq t < 38$ | 32 | | $32 \leq t < 38$ | 59 | |
| $38 \leq t < 44$ | 45 | | $38 \leq t < 44$ | 20 | |
| $44 \leq t < 50$ | 30 | | $44 \leq t < 50$ | 8 | |
| $50 \leq t < 56$ | 5 | | $50 \leq t < 56$ | 2 | |

a) Complete the table, writing in all mid-interval values.

b) Use the mid-interval technique to estimate the mean time for each team.

......................................................................................................................................

......................................................................................................................................

**Q4** The lengths of 25 snakes are measured to the nearest cm, and then grouped in a frequency table.

| Length | 151 - 155 | 156 - 160 | 161 -165 | 166 - 170 | 171 - 175 | Total |
|---|---|---|---|---|---|---|
| frequency | 4 | 8 | 7 | 5 | 1 | 25 |

Which of the following sentences may be true and which have to be false?

a) The median length is 161 cm. ...........................................................................

b) The range is 20 cm. .........................................................................

c) The modal class has 7 snakes.

......................................................................

d) The median length is 158 cm.

......................................................................

*Remember — with grouped data you can't find these values exactly, but you can narrow down the possibilities.*

# Time Series

Two important things you need to spot with time series — trends and seasonality.
A trend is the overall change in the data. Watch out for a repeating pattern —
it means the series is seasonal.

**Q1** Which of the following sets of measurements form time series?

**a)** The average rainfall in Cumbria, measured each day for a year.

**b)** The daily rainfall in European capital cities on Christmas Day, 2000.

**c)** The shoe size of everybody in Class 6C on September 1st, 2001.

**d)** My shoe size (measured every month) from when I was twelve months old
to when I was fourteen years old.

**Q2** **a)** Which two of the following time series are seasonal, and which two are not seasonal?

A

B

C

D

**b)** What are the periods of the time series which are seasonal?

..............................................................................................................

**c)** Describe the trends in the time series which are **not** seasonal.

..............................................................................................................

..............................................................................................................

..............................................................................................................

# Probability

**When you're asked to find the probability of something, always check that your answer is between 0 and 1. If it's not, you know straight away that you've made a mistake.**

**Q1** Write down whether these events are impossible, unlikely, even, likely or certain.

**a)** You will go shopping on Saturday. ................................

**b)** You will live to be 300 years old. ................................

**c)** The next person who comes into the room is female. ................................

**d)** You will be able to see the Moon in the sky tonight. ................................

**Q2** A bag contains ten balls. Five are red, three are yellow and two are green.
What is the probability of picking out:

**a)** A yellow ball? ................................

**b)** A red ball? ................................

**c)** A green ball? ................................

**d)** A red or a green ball? ................................

**e)** A blue ball? ................................

**Q3** Write down the probability of these events happening.
Write each answer as a fraction, as a decimal and as a percentage.
E.g. tossing a head on a fair coin: ½, 0.5, 50%

**a)** Throwing an odd number on a fair six-sided dice. ..........., .........., ...........

**b)** Drawing a black card from a standard pack of playing cards. ..........., .........., ...........

**c)** Drawing a black King from a standard pack of cards. ..........., .........., ...........

**d)** Throwing a prime number on a fair six-sided dice. ..........., .........., ...........

**Q4** Mike and Nick play a game of pool. The probability of Nick winning is 7/10.

**a)** Put an arrow on the probability line below to show the probability of Nick winning.
Label this arrow N.

**b)** Now put an arrow on the probability line to show the probability of Mike winning the game.
Label this arrow M.

0                                                                    1

# Probability

**Q5**   The outcome when a coin is tossed is head (H) or tail (T).
Complete this table of outcomes when two coins are tossed one after the other.

**a)** How many possible outcomes are there? ...........................

**b)** What is the probability of getting 2 heads? ...........................

**c)** What is the probability of getting a head
followed by a tail? ...........................

|          |     | 2ⁿᵈ COIN |     |
|----------|-----|------|-----|
|          |     | **H** | **T** |
| 1ˢᵗ COIN | **H** |      |     |
|          | **T** |      |     |

**Q6**   Lucy has designed a game for the school fair.  Two dice are rolled at the same time and
the scores on the dice are added together.  She needs to work out the probability of all
the possible outcomes so she can decide which outcomes will get a prize.
Complete the table of possible outcomes below.

How many different combinations are there? ...........................

| FIRST DICE \ SECOND DICE | 1 | 2 | 3 | 4 | 5 | 6 |
|-----|---|---|---|---|---|---|
| **1** |   |   |   |   |   |   |
| **2** | 3 |   |   |   |   |   |
| **3** |   |   |   |   |   |   |
| **4** |   |   |   |   |   |   |
| **5** |   |   | 8 |   |   |   |
| **6** |   |   |   |   |   |   |

What is the probability of scoring:

**a)** 2  ...........................

**b)** 6  ...........................

**c)** 10  ...........................

**d)** More than 9  ...........................

**e)** Less than 4  ...........................

**f)** More than 12  ...........................

**g)** Lucy would like to give a prize for any outcome that has a 50% chance of occurring.
Suggest an outcome that has a 50% chance of occurring.

...................................................................................................

**Q7**   Two spinners are spun and the scores are multiplied together.

|          |   | SPINNER 1 |   |   |
|----------|---|---|---|---|
|          |   | **2** | **3** | **4** |
| SPINNER 2 | **3** |   |   |   |
|          | **4** |   |   |   |
|          | **5** |   |   |   |

Fill in this table of possible outcomes.

What is the probability of scoring 12? ...........................

To win you have to score 15 or more.
What is the probability of winning? ...............................

In the exam, you might not be asked to put the "possible outcomes" in a table.  But it's
a good idea to make your own table anyway — that way you don't miss any out.

*SECTION SEVEN — STATISTICS AND PROBABILITY*

# Probability

Well, OK, the probability is that you'd rather not be doing these at all...
still — this is the last page, so I'm sure you'll cope for a bit longer.

**Q8**   The two spinners on the right are spun at the same time.
Find the probability of:

**a)** Spinning an A and a 2. ..............................

**b)** Spinning a 1 and a 3. ..............................

**Q9**   The probability of it raining during the monsoon is ¾, on a particular day.

**a)** What is the probability of it <u>not raining</u>? ................................

**b)** If a monsoon 'season' lasts approximately <u>100 days</u>, how many days are likely to be <u>dry</u>?

.................................................................................................

**Q10**   Imagine you have just made a 6-sided spinner in Design and Technology.
How could you test whether or not it's a fair spinner?

Remember — if the spinner's
fair, the probability of landing
on each side is the same.

.................................................................................................

.................................................................................................

.................................................................................................

**Q11 a)** A biased dice is rolled 40 times.  A six came up 14 times.
Calculate the relative frequency that a six was rolled.

.................................................................................................

**b)** The same dice is rolled another 60 times.  From this, a six came up 24 times.
Calculate the relative frequency that a six was rolled.

.................................................................................................

**c)** Use the data from **a)** and **b)** to make the best estimate you can
of the probability of rolling a six with the dice.

.................................................................................................